C000098056

Essential Maths 9H

Homework Book

Michael White

Elmwood Press

First published 2010 by
Elmwood Press
80 Attimore Road
Welwyn Garden City
Herts. AL8 6LP
Tel. 01707 333232

All rights reserved. No part of this publication may be reproduced, stored in a retrieval system, or transmitted, in any form or by any means, electronic, mechanical, photocopying, recording or otherwise, without permission in writing from the publisher or under licence from the Copyright Licensing Agency Ltd., of 90 Tottenham Court Road, London, WIT 4LP

Any person who commits any unauthorized act in relation to this publication may be liable to criminal prosecution and civil claims for damages.

© Michael White
The moral rights of the author have been asserted.
Database right Elmwood Press (maker)

ISBN 9781 906 622 183

Numerical answers are published in a separate book

Typeset and illustrated by Domex e-Data Pvt. Ltd.
Printed and bound by Bookwell

CONTENTS

UNIT 1

1.1 Working with numbers

Work out, without a calculator

1 $5600 - 314$ **2** 0.7×0.6 **3** 9×0.8 **4** $107 \div 100$

5 0.003×10000 **6** $42.98 \div 7$ **7** $3.46 + 38$ **8** 0.08×0.1

9 18×0.6 **10** $7389 + 874$ **11** $30.96 \div 8$ **12** 5.34×3000

13 $10^3 - 673$ **14** $38.02 \div 100$ **15** $104 \div 16$ **16** $10^4 + 10^3 + 10^2$

17 $130 \div 25$ **18** $0.64 - 0.386$ **19** $20^3 - 20^2$ **20** $0.192 \div 0.6$

21 Tim bakes 144 cakes for a charity stall. The ingredients cost him £16. He sells each cake for 35p. How much money does he make for the charity if he sells all the cakes?

22 Zak made 160 greetings cards which cost him a total of £67.20. How much did each card cost?

23 Put each of the numbers 1, 2, 3, 4 and 5 into the boxes below to make a correct calculation.

$$\boxed{} \times \boxed{} - \boxed{} \times \boxed{} = \boxed{}$$

24 How many 0.15 m lengths of wood can be cut from a piece of wood which is 1.8 m long?

25 Put these three calculations in order of size, starting with the smallest:

$0.8 \div 100$ 0.3×0.002 $5.376 \div 5.369$

    P   Q   R

1 Answer true or false:

(a) $3 + 2 \times 5 = 13$ (b) $8 \times 2 \div 4 = 4$ (c) $9 - 2 \times 3 = 21$

(d) $48 \div 8 \times 2 = 12$ (e) $(8 - 6)^3 - 3 = 3$ (f) $4 + 5^2 \times 2 + 8 = 62$

2 Work out

(a) $16 + 30 \div 6$ (b) $7^2 - 40 \div 8$ (c) $27 - (12 - 5)$

(d) $40 - 2^5$ (e) $5 + 7 \times 3 - 14$ (f) $(8 - 5)^3 + 17$

(g) $48 \div 6 + 2$ (h) $\dfrac{(5^2 - 5) \times 5}{5^2}$ (i) $64 \div (5 - 3)^4$

(j) $(5 + 2^4) \times (4^3 - 8^2)$ (k) $8 + 6^2 \div 4$ (l) $6 + 4^2 \div 8 + 4$

3 Copy and write in brackets so that each calculation below gives the correct answer.

(a) $7 + 6 \times 2 = 26$ (b) $3 + 9 \times 5 = 48$ (c) $28 - 20 \times 4 = 32$

(d) $32 \div 8 - 2 = 2$ (e) $6 + 3 \times 4 - 6 = 12$ (f) $45 \div 5 + 12 - 7 = 14$

(g) $40 - 6 - 10 - 2 = 26$ (h) $28 - 14 - 6 - 3 = 17$

HWK 2M   **Main Book Page 3**

1 Each box below contains a single digit. Copy and complete each calculation.

(a) $\boxed{}\boxed{} \times 14 = 392$ (b) $\boxed{}\boxed{}\boxed{} \div 8 = 46$ (c) $\boxed{}\boxed{}\boxed{}\boxed{} \div 6 = 173$

(d) $\boxed{}\boxed{}\boxed{}\boxed{} - 1468 = 639$ (e) $17 \times \boxed{}\boxed{} = 391$ (f) $\boxed{}\boxed{}^2 \div 32 = 8$

2 In the circle write $+$, $-$, $\times$ or $\div$ to make the calculation correct.

(a) $5 \times 7 \bigcirc 5 = 30$ (b) $8 \bigcirc 10 + 4 = 2$ (c) $54 \div 9 \bigcirc 3 = 9$

(d) $4 \times 10 \bigcirc 6 = 46$ (e) $72 \div 8 \bigcirc 5 = 4$ (f) $28 + 7 \bigcirc 15 = 20$

3 Copy and complete

(a)
```
   4 □ 5
 − 2 9 □
   □ 1 9
```

(b)
```
   3 6 7
 + □ 2 □
   7 □ 6
```

(c)
```
   □ 8 □
 − 1 □ 8
   2 1 6
```

(d) $(12 - 8)(3 + \square) = 8^2 - 2^2 - 24$

(e) $\dfrac{8(6 + \square)}{30 - 6} = 10 - 2 \times 3$

4 Each of these calculations has the same four numbers missing from all four boxes. Find the missing numbers in each calculation.

$\boxed{a} + \boxed{b} \times \boxed{c} - \boxed{d} = 14$

$\boxed{a} \times \boxed{d} - \boxed{c} \times \boxed{b} = 27$

$\boxed{c} + \boxed{b} + \boxed{d} - \boxed{a} = 9$

$\boxed{d} + \boxed{a} \div \boxed{c} - \boxed{b} = 4$

HWK 3M   **Main Book Page 4**

1 Write down the first six multiples of 13.

2 Write down all the factors of 30.

3 Write down all the factors of 48.

4 Which number opposite is a factor of 60 *and* a multiple of 4?

5 Find the highest common factor (HCF) of;

(a) 16 and 72   (b) 30 and 105   (c) 60 and 165

6 Work out

(a) $\sqrt{169}$ (b) $\sqrt[3]{64}$ (c) $\sqrt{(5^2 \times 4^2)}$ (d) $6^3 - 5^3$

7 Find the lowest common multiple (LCM) of;

(a) 8 and 12   (b) 7 and 14   (c) 15 and 25

8 Write down possible values for a and b if

$$a^2 - b^2 = 56$$

9 Sharon thinks of a number which is a factor of 36 and lies between 10 and 15. Myles thinks of a number which is a multiple of 27 and lies between 80 and 90. What is the difference between the two numbers?

10 Chad visits his grandparents on every 12th day. His sister, Megan, visits the grandparents every fortnight. They both visit the grandparents on 3rd March. On what date do they both next visit the grandparents at the same time?

HWK 3E ————————————————————————————— **Main Book Page 5**

1 Write down all the prime numbers between 20 and 30.

2 Copy and complete these prime factor trees.

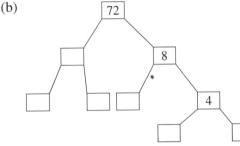

(a) 90 — 45 — 5

(b) 72 — 8 — 4

3 A number n is written as a product of prime numbers such that $n = 2^2 \times 3^2 \times 5$. What is the value of n?

4 Write the following numbers as products of prime numbers:

(a) 28   (b) 120   (c) 150

5 Find the highest common factor of 378 and 420 by writing each number as the product of prime numbers.

6 $882 = 2 \times 3^2 \times 7^2$ and $11550 = 2 \times 3 \times 5^2 \times 7 \times 11$

Find the lowest common multiple of 882 and 11550.

7 Find the lowest common multiple of 819 and 3234.

4

8 Find the highest common factor of 819 and 3234.

9 How many prime numbers smaller than 50 end in 7?

10 The square number 49 can be written as the sum of three prime numbers. Write down these possible prime numbers.

1 £132 is shared in the ratio 5:6. What is the largest share worth?

2 In a restaurant, the ratio of knives to forks is 6:5. There are 210 forks. How many knives are there?

3 Write each ratio in its simplest form

    (a) 32:24   (b) 14:56:35   (c) 51:85:68

4 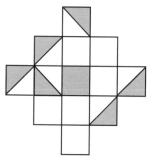 Write down the ratio of (shaded area) : (white area) for this shape.

5 45 loaves of bread are shared between Dan, Jane and Tariq in the ratio 3:2:4. How many loaves of bread does each person get?

6 64 CDs are shared between Tom, Rita and John in the ratio 8:3:5. How many CDs does each person get?

7 Write the following ratios in their simplest form:

    (a) 5p to £1   (b) 40 cm to 2 m   (c) 250 g to 1 kg

8 $A\hat{D}C = 80$ in a quadrilateral ABCD. $B\hat{C}D$ is double $B\hat{A}D$ and $A\hat{B}C$ is five times greater than $B\hat{A}D$. Find the size of $B\hat{A}D$.

9 Wayne has 36 pairs of socks. 10 pairs of socks are blue. What proportion of the socks are *not* blue? Give your answer as a fraction.

1 The ratio of beer to lemonade in a shandy drink is 3:2. How much beer is used with 6 litres of lemonade?

2 A scarf is made from blue and yellow stripes. $\frac{4}{7}$ of the scarf is blue. What is the ratio of blue to yellow?

3 A recipe for 12 cakes requires 300 g of plain flour. How much plain flour is needed to make 15 cakes?

4

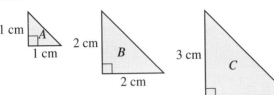

Write down the following ratios:
(a) area A : area C
(b) area B : area C
(c) area C : area B

5 Darren and Max work in a circus. They are paid in the ratio of their heights. Darren is 2 m tall and Max is 1.6 m tall. How much is Max paid if Darren is paid £360 each week?

6 Find the value of *n* in each equation.

(a) $n:5 = 12:15$ (b) $8:n = 4:7$ (c) $n:3 = 48:n$ (d) $100:n = n:4$

7

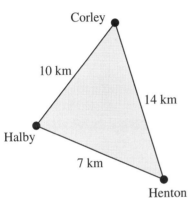

These villages are marked on a map with a scale of 1:200000.

What is the length on the map:
(a) from Henton to Halby?
(b) from Halby to Corley?
(c) from Corley to Henton?

8 The rectangular field opposite is drawn on a map with a scale of 1:5000. What is the actual area of this field?

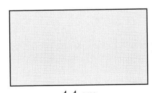

9 Mia is planning a walk. She has to use two maps. She wants to walk from Garby to Hendleford then from Hendleford to Wendon. The first map with a scale of 1:20000 shows the distance from Garby to Hendleford is 35 cm. The second map with a scale of 1:50000 shows the distance from Hendleford to Wendon is 11 cm. What will be the actual total distance of Mia's walk from Garby to Wendon?

10 A map has scale 1:20000. What is the actual area of a playing field whose area on the map is 6 cm²? (Give your answer in km²)

| HWK 5M | Main Book Page 7 |

Use a calculator to work out each answer correct to 2 decimal places.

1 $5.312 + \dfrac{2 \cdot 4}{3 \cdot 7}$

2 $\dfrac{5 \cdot 18 + 0 \cdot 196}{2 \cdot 09}$

3 $\dfrac{4 \cdot 317 - 1 \cdot 096}{2 \cdot 68 \times 0 \cdot 34}$

6

4 $0.73 + (0.169 \times 2.3)$

5 $\dfrac{5.7}{2.3} + 3.182$

6 $\dfrac{3.2}{1.916} + \dfrac{2.17}{4.4}$

7 $\dfrac{1.13 \times 2.77}{4.49 + 3.16}$

8 $\dfrac{(1.7 - 0.29)^2}{3.08}$

9 $\dfrac{1.47}{3.6} + 3.14^2$

10 Work out the answers and place each question below in order of size, starting with the smallest:

$$\boxed{\dfrac{7.14^2 - 6.39}{1.04}}$$
A

$$\boxed{\dfrac{5.173 + 2.53}{0.012}}$$
B

$$\boxed{\dfrac{1.93 \times 2.07}{5.17 \times 3.16}}$$
C

11 A machine cuts 12 rectangular pieces of card every minute. Find the exact total area of card that the machine cuts in one hour.

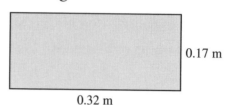

0.17 m

0.32 m

12 Calculate to one decimal place:

$$\dfrac{3.6 + 2.14^2}{5.07 - 1.89} + \dfrac{2.178}{0.67^2}$$

HWK 5E ———————————————————— **Main Book Page 8**

Use a calculator to work out

1 $\dfrac{5}{7} - \dfrac{1}{4}$

2 $\dfrac{5}{9} + \dfrac{2}{7}$

3 $\dfrac{2}{3} \times \dfrac{5}{8}$

4 $\dfrac{1}{9} - \dfrac{1}{11}$

5 $\dfrac{3}{8} \div \dfrac{7}{9}$

6 $2\dfrac{1}{3} + 1\dfrac{3}{5}$

7 $3\dfrac{1}{2} - 1\dfrac{5}{6}$

8 $\left(\dfrac{1}{2} + \dfrac{1}{3}\right) \times \dfrac{1}{3}$

9 $\dfrac{4}{5}$ of $\left(\dfrac{2}{3}\right)^2$

10 $\left(\dfrac{3}{10} - \dfrac{1}{9}\right) \div \dfrac{3}{4}$

11 $\left(\dfrac{3}{4}\right)^2 + \left(\dfrac{1}{3}\right)^3$

12 $\left(3\dfrac{3}{4} - 1\dfrac{2}{3}\right)^2$

13

ham	£6.80/kg
bread roll	38p each
apples	£2.70 for 10
cheese	£5.30/kg

(a) Calculate the cost of 4 bread rolls, 3 apples, $\dfrac{1}{2}$ kg of cheese and $\dfrac{1}{4}$ kg of ham.

(b) How much change from £10 will Jennie get if she buys 0.4 kg of ham, 7 apples, 0.3 kg of cheese and 6 bread rolls?

14 Copy and complete

(a) $\boxed{} + 2\dfrac{1}{5} = 4\dfrac{19}{20}$

(b) $\boxed{} \times \dfrac{1}{8} + \dfrac{2}{3} = \dfrac{89}{120}$

(c) $\left(\boxed{} + 2\dfrac{2}{3}\right) \times \dfrac{1}{6} = \dfrac{47}{72}$

(d) $\left(\boxed{}^3 + \dfrac{1}{3}\right) \div \dfrac{2}{5} = 1\dfrac{7}{48}$

1 Work out

(a) $7 - (-3)$ (b) $6 \times (-8)$ (c) $(-10) \div (-5)$ (d) $-8 + 6$

(e) $(-7) \times (-4)$ (f) $-5 - 8$ (g) $(-5)^2$ (h) $(-20) \div 4$

(i) $4 \times (-3)^2$ (j) $-9 + 7$ (k) $(-3) \times (-8)$ (l) $35 \div (-7)$

(m) $(-36) \div (-9)$ (n) $-16 - (-4)$ (o) $(-6) \times 9$ (p) $(-8)^2$

2 Which question below gives the largest answer?

A $\boxed{(-3) \times (-2)}$ B $\boxed{(-2)^2}$ C $\boxed{8 \times (-3)}$

D $\boxed{-6 + 11}$ E $\boxed{4 \times (-1)^2}$

3 Work out

(a) $\frac{1}{2} \times (-6)$ (b) $(-\frac{1}{4}) \times 12$ (c) $5 \div (-\frac{1}{2})$ (d) $-1 - (-\frac{1}{2})$

4 Find the value of

$-8 + (-3) + 10 - 4 - (-7) - 2$

5 Which question below gives the odd answer out?

P $\boxed{(-3)^2 - 10}$ Q $\boxed{(-24) \div (-4)}$ R $\boxed{3 - 9 - (-5)}$

6 Find the value of

$(-8) \times (-7) - (-2) \times 3$

7 Work out

(a) $(-2)^3$ (b) $(-3)^3$ (c) $3 \times (-4)^2$ (d) $(3 \times (-4))^2$

(e) $(-3)^3 \times (-5)$ (f) $(-5)^2 \times (-2)^3$ (g) $(-2)^4$ (h) $\frac{1}{8}$ of $(-8)^2$

(i) $\frac{(-4)^2}{(-2)^3}$ (j) $\frac{(-1)^4 + (-3)^2}{7 + (-2)}$ (k) $\frac{(-5)^2}{2 \times (-5)}$ (l) $(-2\frac{1}{2})^2 - (-1\frac{1}{3})$

Do not use a calculator.

Work out

1 68×37 **2** 184×46 **3** 216×29 **4** 38×528

5 $918 \div 27$ **6** $1152 \div 32$ **7** $817 \div 43$ **8** $2356 \div 62$

9 A tin of chocolates costs £5.32. How much will 12 tins cost?

10 48 pencils cost £22.08. How much does each pencil cost?

11 Work out the area of this rectangle.

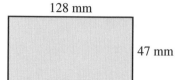

128 mm

47 mm

12 There are 11 rows of chairs in a school assembly. Each row has 29 chairs. How many chairs are there in total?

13 One day a factory produces 400 clocks. The clocks are packed into boxes. What is the least number of boxes needed if one box can hold 15 clocks?

14

Shop A	Shop B	Shop C
34 packets of crisps for £14.28	41 packets of crisps for £15.99	52 packets of crisps for £21.32

Put these shops in order according to the cost of a packet of crisps, starting with the cheapest.

HWK 8M ────────────────────────── **Main Book Page 11**

1 Five pairs of numbers below are equal in value. Write down each pair. (Beware: there are two odd numbers out!)

$$0.31 \qquad 40\% \qquad \frac{2}{25} \qquad 0.06$$

$$8\% \qquad \frac{7}{20} \qquad \frac{31}{100} \qquad 60\%$$

$$\frac{3}{5} \qquad 0.04 \qquad 0.35 \qquad 0.4$$

2 Trevor is interested in buying one of two cars. The Corsa is priced at £7500 and the Galant costs £8600. Trevor is offered a 15% discount on the Corsa and a 25% discount on the Galant. Which car is cheaper and by how much?

3 Write in order, smallest first.

(a) $0.43, \frac{2}{5}, 42\%$ (b) $\frac{3}{25}, 11\%, 0.08$

4 Matt spends 2.5% of a complete day travelling to and from school. How many minutes is this?

5 The table below shows how many boys and girls there are in five year 9 classes in Henton High School. What percentage of all the children in year 9 are girls? Give your answer to one decimal place.

class	9A	9B	9C	9D	9E
boys	17	15	17	13	14
girls	14	15	18	18	16

6 Work out $\frac{2}{3}$ of 6% of 2% of $\left(\frac{3}{2}\right)^4$

7 What percentage of the prime numbers less than 20 are also factors of 60?

1.2 Using algebra

HWK 1M   **Main Book Page 13**

Simplify the following expressions.

1 $5y \times 3$ | **2** $4x \times 9$ | **3** $30a \div 6$ | **4** $24p \div 8$

5 $56m \div 7$ | **6** $8 \times 5y$ | **7** $4 \times 9n$ | **8** $27m \div 9$

9 $p \times p$ | **10** $4n \times n$ | **11** $y \times 5y$ | **12** $8a \times 2a$

13 $4y \times 6y$ | **14** $18m \div 6$ | **15** $45a \div 15$ | **16** $3p \times 10p$

17 $32a \div 4$ | **18** $y \times 8y$ | **19** $5a \times 4b$ | **20** $9p \times 6q$

21 $48p \div 6$ | **22** $7m \times 9n$ | **23** $15y \times 7$ | **24** $6a \times 6a$

25 $20n^2 \div 4n$ | **26** $(7m)^2$ | **27** $\dfrac{6mn}{3n}$ | **28** $\dfrac{ab^2c}{abc^2}$

29 $5m + m + 3m$ | **30** $\dfrac{4m + 12n}{4}$ | **31** $\dfrac{(4n)^2}{8n}$ | **32** $\dfrac{3n^2 - 8n}{n}$

33 Answer true or false:

(a) $5n \times n = 6n$ | (b) $22y \div 2 = 11y$ | (c) $5 \times 7m = 35m$

(d) $42m \div 6 = 8m$ | (e) $2a \times 3b = 5ab$ | (f) $4a \times 4a = 8a^2$

HWK 1E   **Main Book Page 13**

Remove the brackets from these expressions.

1 $3(n + 8)$ | **2** $4(x - 3)$ | **3** $3(4n + 3)$ | **4** $-3(2 + 9x)$

5 $-9(2m - 7)$ | **6** $5(3m + 5n - 7)$ | **7** $-4(2x - 5)$ | **8** $6(n^2 + 5n - 3)$

Remove the brackets and simplify.

9 $5(4a + 5) + 6(3a - 2)$ | **10** $6(5x + 3) - 4(2x - 5)$ | **11** $4(6n + 5) - 2(10n + 9)$

12 $4y + 6(2y - 1) + 3$ | **13** $5(4x + 1) - 3(5x - 2)$ | **14** $8(n + 7) + 4(3n + 2) - 9n$

15 $8m + 4(2m + 3) - 10m$ | **16** $5(3y + 9) - 4(y + 6) + 10$

10

17 Write down an expression for the total area of these three rectangles. Simplify your answer.

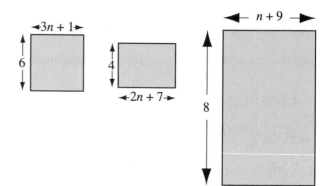

Copy and complete by filling in the boxes.

18 $4(\square - \square) = 12m - 28$

19 $\square(2x + \square) = 16x + 24$

20 $\square(\square - \square + 2) = 20n - 45m + 10$

21 $7(\square - 5b - \square) = 14a - 35b - 21c$

22 $\square - (2 - 5a) = 6 + \square$

23 $3(2x + 5y + \square) + \square = \square + 19y + 3$

HWK 2M   **Main Book Page 14**

1 In the expression $3(n - 4)^2$, the operations are performed in the following order:

$n \rightarrow \boxed{-4} \rightarrow \boxed{\text{square}} \rightarrow \boxed{\times 3} \rightarrow$

Draw similar diagrams to show the correct order of operations for the following expressions.

(a) $5(6n + 4)$ (b) $\dfrac{n^2 - 9}{7}$ (c) $(4n + 6)^2 - 5$ (d) $\dfrac{(5n - 2)^2 + 6}{8}$

2 Write down the expression produced by each of the diagrams below.

(a) $n \rightarrow \boxed{\times 4} \rightarrow \boxed{+9} \rightarrow \boxed{\times 5} \rightarrow$

(b) $n \rightarrow \boxed{\text{square}} \rightarrow \boxed{-6} \rightarrow \boxed{\times 3} \rightarrow \boxed{+1} \rightarrow$

(c) $n \rightarrow \boxed{+4} \rightarrow \boxed{\text{square}} \rightarrow \boxed{\times 4} \rightarrow \boxed{\div 7} \rightarrow$

In questions **3** to **20** answer 'true' or 'false'.

3 $a \times b = ba$

4 $n \times 4 = 4n$

5 $n \times n \times n = n^3$

6 $x - y = y - x$

7 $p^2 = p + p$

8 $3(n + 1) = 3n + 1$

9 $4y \times y = 4y^2$

10 $4(m + n) = 4m + n$

11 $a \div 4 = \dfrac{a}{4}$

12 $5 \div n = \dfrac{n}{5}$

13 $n^3 + n^2 = n^5$

14 $n^2 \times n^2 = n^4$

15 $\dfrac{6a}{3} = 2a$

16 $\dfrac{a^3}{a} = a^2$

17 $\dfrac{4(m - 2)}{2} = 2m - 2$

18 $(a + b)^2 = a^2 + b^2$

19 $10n \div n = 10$

20 $\dfrac{m^2 + n^2}{2} = m + n$

HWK 2E ———————————————————————— **Main Book Page 16**

Remove the brackets and simplify.

1 $y(y + 2)$ **2** $n(n - 3)$ **3** $a(a - 9)$ **4** $3n(n + 2)$

5 $5x(x - 3)$ **6** $9m(m + 4)$ **7** $2y(y - 10)$ **8** $4n(6 + n)$

9 $2a(3a + 4)$ **10** $4x(2x - 1)$ **11** $m(4m + 7)$ **12** $6x(1 + 3x)$

13 $5y(2y - 6)$ **14** $3n(8 + 4n)$ **15** $6y(2y - 8)$ **16** $8n(4n + 9)$

Copy and complete by filling in the boxes.

17 $\square(a - 6) = \square - 18a$ **18** $\square(n + 2) = 5n^2 + \square$ **19** $3m(\square + \square) = 6m^2 + 3m$

20 $\square(4y - 3) = 8y^2 - \square$ **21** $\square(\square - 4) = m^2 - 4m$ **22** $2(\square + 2) + \square(a + 6) = 10a + 28$

23 $5(\square - 2) + 6(2n + 3) = 27n + \square$ **24** $\square(5n + 6) + 3(\square + 4n) = 32n + 27$

HWK 3M ———————————————————————— **Main Book Page 17**

$A = x + 4$ $B = 4x - 3$ $C = 2x + 5$ $D = 3x$

Find the value of each expression below, in terms of x. Give your answers in their simplest form.
For example: $2C + B - D = 2(2x + 5) + 4x - 3 - 3x$
$$= 4x + 10 + 4x - 3 - 3x$$
$$= 5x + 7$$

1 $A + B$ **2** $3A + C$ **3** $A + C + D$

4 $2C - D$ **5** $2B + 3D$ **6** $4A + 2C + 4D$

7 $3A + D - C$ **8** $3C + B + 5D$ **9** $5A - B$

10 $C + 2D - A$ **11** $5C - 2D + A$ **12** $2A + B + 3C + 2D$

13 Answer 'true' or 'false'.

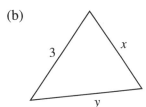

(a) 5, n, area = $5n$

(b) 3, x, y, perimeter = $3xy$

(c) $2m$, $2m$, area = $8m$

14 Answer 'true' or 'false'.

(a)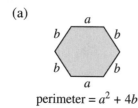

perimeter = $a^2 + 4b$

(b)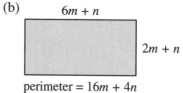

$6m + n$

$2m + n$

perimeter = $16m + 4n$

(c)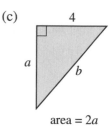

4

a

b

area = $2a$

15

4x   5x

x + 4

3x

Find a simplified expression for the surface area of this triangular prism.

HWK 4M ──────────────────────────────── **Main Book Page 18**

Solve the equations

1 $3x + 6 = 0$ **2** $4 = 3 + 5x$ **3** $1 = 13 + 6x$ **4** $8 + 9x = 9$

5 $40 + 7x = 12$ **6** $8x - 3 = 4$ **7** $20 + 3x = 2$ **8** $2 = 7x - 4$

9 $12 = 4x + 9$ **10** $2 = 10x - 7$ **11** $2 = 4x + 18$ **12** $6x + 15 = 9$

Now solve these equations

13 $16 - 2x = 11 + 3x$ **14** $29 + 5x = 56 - 4x$ **15** $9x - 4 = 2x + 1$

16 $11x + 7 = 8x - 5$ **17** $9x - 12 = 4x + 18$ **18** $2x - 8 = 3x + 23$

19 $17 + 6x = 3x + 2$ **20** $5x + 16 = 4x + 1$ **21** $8x - 14 = 4x + 4$

22 $8 - 2x = 8 + 4x$ **23** $4 + 11x = 10 - x$ **24** $2 - 9x = 10 - 5x$

25

$n + 16$ $4n - 2$

$2n + 3$

Find the actual perimeter of this isosceles triangle.
All measurements are in cm.

HWK 4E ———————————————————————————— **Main Book Page 19**

Solve the equations

1 $3(3x + 4) = 8(2x - 2)$ **2** $2(5x + 3) = 13(3x - 4)$ **3** $4(3x - 2) = 8(x + 2)$

4 $7(4x + 1) = 13(3x - 2)$ **5** $5(6x - 7) = 1 + 12x$ **6** $10(2x - 3) = 7(x + 5)$

Now solve these equations

7 $6(5x - 4) = 31(x - 1)$ **8** $4(7x + 2) = 38(1 + x)$ **9** $3(x + 6) = 2(2x + 11)$

10 $5(2x + 5) = 7(7 + 2x)$ **11** $3(6x - 1) = 8x + 4$ **12** $2(3 + 4x) = 3(2x + 5)$

13 $4(2x + 1) - 5(x - 3) = 17$ **14** $20 - 4(3x + 2) = 9$ **15** $7(2 + 3x) - 3(5x - 4) = 23$

HWK 5M/5E ———————————————————————————— **Main Book Page 19**

1 If I add 8 to the number and then multiply the result by 6, I get the same answer as when I add 58 to the number. Form an equation then find the number.

2 If I multiply the number by 7, subtract 5 and then multiply the result by 2, the answer I get is the same as when I multiply the number by 11 and then add 20. Form an equation then find the number.

3 Angle A in this isosceles triangle is 60° more than angle B. Find the actual values of the three angles.

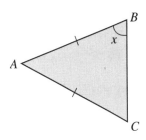

4 Find five consecutive *even* numbers whose sum is 300.

5 The table shows how much pocket money each person gets each week. The mean weekly pocket money is £15. How much does each person actually receive?

Name	Pocket money (£)
Chloe	$3n + 1$
Matt	$2(3n - 4)$
Amber	$4(n + 6)$
Dan	$7n + 3$

6

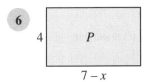

The area of rectangle P is equal to the area of rectangle Q. What is the actual total area of rectangles P and Q? All measurements are in cm.

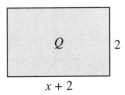

7 Rhian has $(x + 2)$ 250 g weights and $(x + 7)$ 2 kg weights. How many of each type of weight does Rhian have if the total weight is 32.5 kg?

8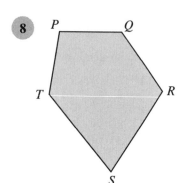

The angles in a pentagon add up to 540°.
Angle T is 10° more than angle S which is 10° more than angle R which is 10° more than angle Q which is 10° more than angle P. Find the value of angle P.

9 If I treble a number, subtract 8 and then divide the result by 5, I get the same answer as when I subtract the number from 14 and then divide the result by 4. Form an equation then find the number.

10 The length of this rectangle is three times its width. Find the actual perimeter of this rectangle. All measurements are in cm.

$2x + 3$ $3x - 1$

HWK 6M/6E   **Main Book Page 21**

Copy and complete.

1 $12a - 15 = 3(\Box - \Box)$

2 $14m + 21 = \Box (2m + \Box)$

3 $10n - 30 = \Box(\Box - \Box)$

4 $10x^2 - xy = x(\Box - \Box)$

5 $6a^2 + 4a = 2a(\Box + 2)$

6 $3a^2 + 6ab = \Box(a + 2b)$

Factorise the following expressions.

7 $15x - 35y$

8 $21a + 49b$

9 $20m + 45n$

10 $8m + 18n + 6p$

11 $9a + 21b - 12c$

12 $15p + 45q - 10r$

13 $30 + 18b - 36c$

14 $8m - 2n - 8p$

15 $20x - 16y + 24z$

Now factorise these.

16 $x^2 + 5x$

17 $9y^2 + 7y$

18 $a - 3a^2$

19 $8x^2 - 12x$

20 $ab - a^2$

21 $9n^2 + 3n$

22 $16a^2 - 12ab$

23 $20n^2 + 6n$

24 $10xy + 5xyz$

25 $5x^2 + 8xy$

26 $6mnp - 8mn$

27 $14ab - 21abc$

28 $3p^2 + 12pqr$

29 $n^3 + mn$

30 $x^3 + x$

1.3 Congruent shapes and construction

———————————————— **Main Book Page 24**

Remember: Congruent shapes are exactly the same in every respect.

1 Use ruler and compasses only to construct an equilateral triangle of side length 7 cm.

2 (a) Construct the triangle shown opposite.
(b) Bisect angle ABC using ruler and compasses only.
(c) Measure the angle you have just constructed.

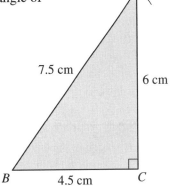

3 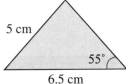 Construct the triangle shown. You are given SSA. Show that you can construct two different triangles with the sides and angle given.

4 State whether each pair of triangles are congruent. Give the conditions for congruency if they are congruent (SSS, SAS, ASA or RHS).

(a)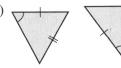

(b)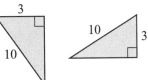

(c)

(d)

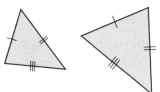

5 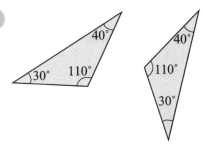 Are these two triangles congruent? Give a reason for your answer.

6 Carys walks 8 km north then 3 km due west. Construct a diagram then find out how far Carys is from her starting position A (ie. what is the direct distance from A to C?)

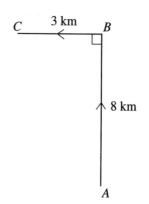

7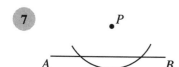

Copy the diagram opposite. Use ruler and compasses only to construct a perpendicular line from point P to the line AB, (a clue is given in the diagram)

1.4 Geometrical reasoning

HWK 1M ──────────────────────────────── **Main Book Page 27**

1 Name this shape.

2 Which shape has more lines of symmetry – a rectangle or a parallelogram?

3 Copy this diagram. Join the points and complete the shape to make a trapezium.

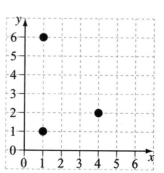

4 Answer 'true' or 'false':

'The diagonals of a parallelogram are equal in length'.

5 Find the angles marked with letters.

(a)
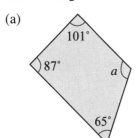

(b)
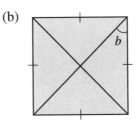

(c)
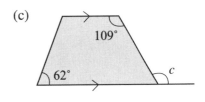

(d)
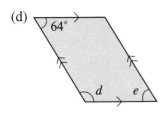

(e)
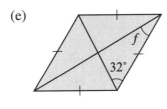

(f)
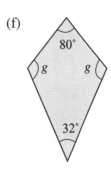

(g)
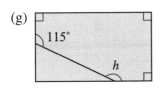

(h)
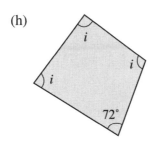

(i)
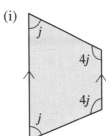

6
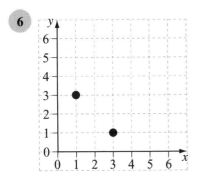

Copy this diagram.

Using the two points shown as vertices (corners) of a kite, complete a drawing of the kite.

7 In which of the following shapes are the diagonals perpendicular to each other?

(square)　(rectangle)　(kite)　(rhombus)　(parallelogram)　(trapezium)

HWK 1E ——————————————————— **Main Book Page 28**

Find the angles marked with letters.

1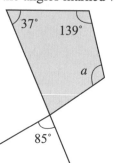
37°
139°
a
85°

2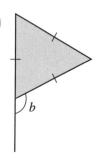
b

3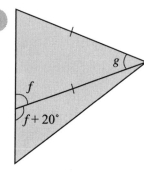
3*c*
c + 15°
c

4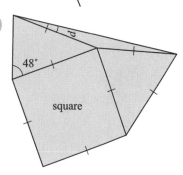
d
48°
square

5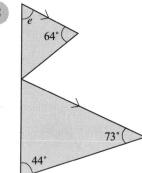
e
64°
73°
44°

6
g
f
f + 20°

7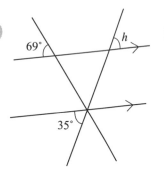
69°
h
35°

8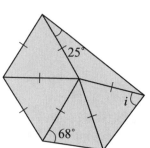
25°
i
68°

9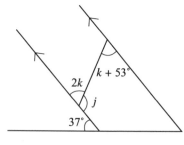
2*k*
k + 53°
j
37°

10 Draw a triangle PQR with PR̂Q = 82°. Point X lies on QR so that PX bisects QP̂R. Find the size of PX̂R if PQ = QR. Give reasons for your answer.

HWK 2M ——————————————————— **Main Book Page 30**

> Remember: for a polygon with *n* sides:
>
> sum of interior angles = (*n* − 2) × 180°

1 Find the value of (*n* − 2) × 180° when *n* = 14.

2 Find the sum of the angles in a polygon with
  (a) 12 sides   (b) 16 sides   (c) 20 sides

3 Find the sum of all the angles in this polygon with 8 sides then find the value of angle *x*.

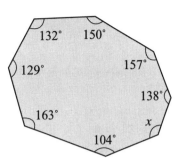

4 All the angles in a regular polygon are equal. Find the sum of all the angles in a regular decagon (10 sides) then find the size of one interior angle.

5 Find the angles marked with letters.

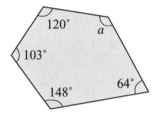

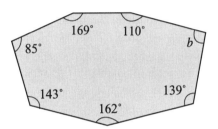

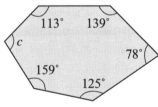

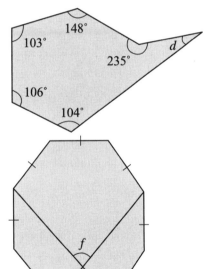

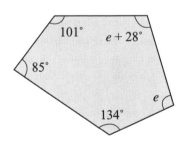

| **HWK 2E** | **Main Book Page 31** |

Remember: the sum of the exterior angles of a polygon is 360°

1 Find the size of each exterior angle of a regular octagon.

2 (a) Calculate the size of each exterior angle for a regular pentagon.
(b) Find the size of each interior angle for a regular pentagon.

20

3 (a) Find the exterior angles of regular polygons with (i) 20 sides (ii) 30 sides

(b) Find the interior angle of the above polygons.

4 The diagram shows some of the interior angles of a regular polygon.

(a) Write down the size of an exterior angle for this polygon,

(b) How many sides has this polygon?

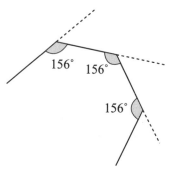

5 Each exterior angle of a regular polygon is 40°. How many sides has the polygon?

6

In the diagram x is the exterior angle of a regular polygon. How many sides has the polygon?

$x + 132°$ x

7

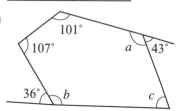

101°

107° a 43°

36° b c

Find the values of angles a, b and c.

8 A polygon with 9 sides (a nonagon) has 8 equal angles x and one angle $2x$. Find the value of x.

9 A regular pentagon is attached to a regular hexagon as shown. Find the value of angle x.

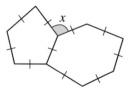

10 In the diagram opposite, O is the centre of a regular polygon. Find the value of angle x.

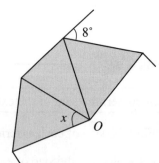

11 One third of the exterior angles of a polygon are 6°, one third are 15° and the remaining third are 24°. How many sides has the polygon?

1.5 Data handling

1 Terry does 3 spelling tests. The mean test mark is 15 and his median test mark is 14. What are the other two test results if the range is 7?

2 The mean weight of 5 people is 68 kg. One person leaves the group. The mean weight of the remaining 4 people is 70 kg. How much did the person who left the group weigh?

3 Ann, Michael and Sasha are given an 8 week trial to sell computers. One person will then be given a job at the end of this time period. The number of computers they sell each week is shown below:

Week	1	2	3	4	5	6	7	8
Ann	4	6	1	7	3	6	7	6
Sasha	7	9	3	5	7	4	8	5
Michael	10	6	2	12	2	10	1	5

(number of computers sold.)

(a) Find the mean and range for each person.

(b) The job is given to the person who sells the most computers but is also the most *consistent* seller. Who gets the job? *Explain* why.

4 25 people were asked how often they had filled their car with petrol during the previous fortnight. The results are shown in the table below.

number of fills	0	1	2	3	4	5	6
frequency	1	3	7	5	4	2	3

Find (a) the mean number of fills

  (b) the modal number of fills (ie. the most common number of fills)

  (c) the median number of fills

5 This back-to-back stem and leaf diagram shows the ages of people in two pubs on one particular night.

The Crown   The Mitre

```
  9 9 9 9 8 8 8  |1|  8 8 9
  9 9 8 6 3 3 3 2  |2|  0 1 1 1 4 7 8
      8 8 5 5 4 0  |3|  2 2 5 7 8 9
          7 6 6 3 1  |4|  3 7 7
                4 2  |5|  4 8 9 9
                     |6|  2 6
                     |7|  3 4
```

| 4\|5 = 54 | | 3\|7 = 37 |

(a) Find the range and median age for The Mitre.

(b) Find the range and median age for The Crown.

(c) Write a sentence to compare the ages of the people in the two pubs.

6 Some bags of flour in a shop were weighed. The table below shows the results. Calculate the mean weight of the bags of flour.

weight (g)	497	498	499	500	501	502
number of bags	2	7	17	36	33	5

HWK 2M/2E ——————————————— **Main Book Page 37**

1 Calculate an estimate for the mean for the information shown in each table.

(a)

Height (cm)	mid-point	Frequency
110–20	115	8
120–130		19
130–140		14
140–150		6
150–160		3

(b)

Length (m)	Mid-point	Frequency
0–0.5	0.25	3
0.5–1		1
1–1.5		7
1.5–2		3
2–2.5		4
2.5–3		2

2 The times taken by runners in a 1500 m race are recorded in this table.

(a) Calculate an estimate for the mean time taken by the runners.

(b) *Explain* why your answer is only an *estimate* of the mean weight.

Time (s)	Mid-point	Frequency
225–230		1
230–235		3
235–240		6
240–245		7
245–250		2
250–255		1

3 Some young people were asked how much they earned in their Saturday part-time jobs.
The mean amount of money was £26.20. Use the information opposite to find the value of n.

Money (£'s)	Frequency
10–20	5
20–30	n
30–40	8

4 The weights of some people were measured and the information is shown in the table. Find the value of x if the mean weight is 62.5 kg.

Weight (kg)	Frequency
40–50	7
50–60	13
60–70	8
70–80	x
80–90	5

1 Here is a frequency polygon showing the heights of a group of young people.

(a) How many young people are there in the group?

(b) How many people are more than 160 cm tall?

(c) What fraction of the people are between 170 cm and 180 cm tall?

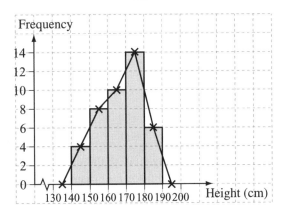

2 Draw a frequency polygon for the distribution of weights shown opposite for some dogs from a local kennels.

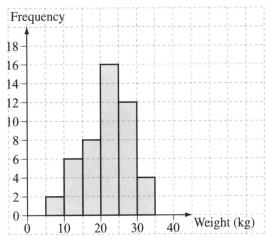

3
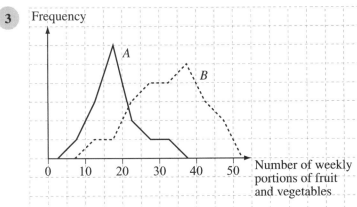

Two groups of people were asked how many portions of fruit and vegetables they ate last week. The results are shown in the frequency polygons above.

Describe the differences between the information shown for group A and group B. Which group of people do you think generally eat more healthily?

4 The weekly money earned by a group of sixteen year olds and a group of eighteen year olds for their holiday part-time jobs is shown in the tables opposite.

Sixteen year olds	
money (£)	frequency
10–20	2
20–30	5
30–40	8
40–50	9
50–60	6
60–70	1

eighteen year olds	
money (£)	frequency
40–50	1
50–60	2
60–70	4
70–80	5
80–90	9
90–100	7
100–110	3

Using the same axes, with the money from £0 to £120, draw frequency polygons for the money earned by the sixteen year olds and for the money earned by the eighteen year olds.

Describe briefly the main differences between the two frequency polygons.

HWK 4M **Main Book Page 43**

1 This cumulative frequency graph shows the money earned by 100 young people in their part-time jobs each week.

(a) What was the median amount of money earned?

(b) Find the upper and lower quartiles.

(c) Find the interquartile range.

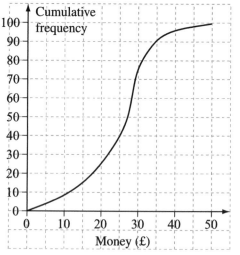

2 The two cumulative frequency graphs below show the heights of two groups of people.

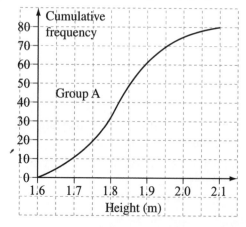

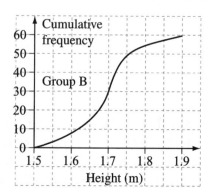

(a) How many people were in group A and how many people were in group B.

(b) Find the median height for each group.

(c) Find the upper and lower quartiles for each group.

(d) Find the interquartile range for each group.

(e) Compare the heights of the people in group A to those in group B.

1.6 Multiplying brackets

HWK 1M ———————————————————— **Main Book Page 45**

Remove the brackets and simplify.

1 $(x + 4)(x + 2)$ **2** $(x + 9)(x + 3)$ **3** $(x + 6)(x - 4)$ **4** $(x + 7)(x - 5)$

5 $(x + 2)(x + 8)$ **6** $(x - 3)(x - 5)$ **7** $(x + 4)(x + 4)$ **8** $(x + 4)^2$

9 $(x + 7)^2$ **10** $(x - 9)(x + 5)$ **11** $(x - 6)(x - 8)$ **12** $(x + 8)^2$

13 $(x - 1)(x - 3)$ **14** $(x + 5)(x - 4)$ **15** $(x - 3)(x + 7)$ **16** $(x - 9)(x + 1)$

17 $(x - 3)^2$ **18** $(x - 6)^2$

HWK 1E ———————————————————— **Main Book Page 45**

Remove both sets of brackets and simplify.

1 $(x + 5)(x + 2) + (x + 6)(x + 3)$ **2** $(x - 2)(x - 7) + (x + 5)(x + 1)$

3 $(4x + 3)(x + 3) + (x - 2)(x - 4)$ **4** $x(x + 6) + (2x + 3)(x + 8)$

5 $(5x + 1)(x - 4) + 3x(x - 2)$ **6** $(x + 7)^2 - x(x + 5)$

7 $(3x + 7)(4x + 1) + (x + 3)^2$ **8** $(5x - 4)(2x + 3) - 2x(x - 4)$

9 The area of the rectangle opposite is written inside it. Write down an expression for the perimeter of the rectangle and simplify it.

$x^2 + 9x + 20$ | $x + 5$

10 Repeat question **9** for each of the two rectangles shown below.

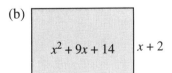

(a) $x + 6$ | $x^2 + 8x + 12$

(b) $x^2 + 9x + 14$ | $x + 2$

11 Copy and complete:

(a) $x^2 + 10x + 21 = (x + 7)(\quad)$ (b) $x^2 - 2x - 24 = (x - 6)(\quad)$

(c) $x^2 + 10x + 9 = (\quad)(\quad)$ (d) $x^2 - 3x - 28 = (\quad)(\quad)$

26

Solve the equations.

1 $(x + 6)(x + 3) = (x + 2)(x + 6)$

2 $(5x + 3)(x + 4) = 5x(x + 8)$

3 $(2x + 5)(3x + 1) = (x - 4)(6x - 1)$

4 $(x + 5)^2 = x(x - 2)$

5 $(3x + 2)^2 = (9x + 2)(x + 3)$

6 $(x + 4)^2 + (x - 3)^2 = 2x(x + 4)$

7 Find x for each of the triangles shown.

(a)
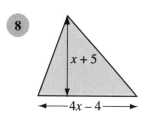

(b)
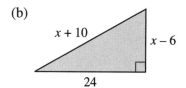

8
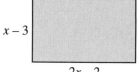
The area of this triangle is twice the area of this square. Find x.
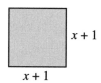

9 The sum of the areas of the two rectangles is equal to the area of the square. Find x.

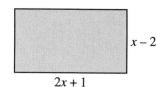
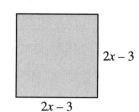

10 The distance s metres of an object from a fixed point after time t seconds is given by the formula

$$s = 4t^2$$

After T seconds, the distance is s_1. Two seconds later the object has moved a further 96 m away from the fixed point. Find the value of T.

UNIT 2

2.1 Using fractions

Work out without a calculator and give the answer in its simplest form.

1. $\frac{8}{9} - \frac{1}{2}$ 2. $\frac{9}{10} - \frac{7}{8}$ 3. $\frac{3}{11} + \frac{2}{5}$ 4. $\frac{5}{9} + \frac{3}{20}$

5. $\frac{4}{7} \times \frac{3}{8}$ 6. $\frac{5}{6} \times \frac{9}{20}$ 7. $\frac{7}{10} \div \frac{4}{5}$ 8. $\frac{3}{4} \div \frac{11}{12}$

9. $2\frac{3}{4} - \frac{8}{9}$ 10. $1\frac{2}{3} + 1\frac{3}{4}$ 11. $3\frac{1}{4} - 1\frac{1}{6}$ 12. $4\frac{2}{3} - 2\frac{5}{8}$

13. $3\frac{1}{4} \times 1\frac{3}{5}$ 14. $5\frac{1}{2} \times 1\frac{3}{5}$ 15. $1\frac{3}{4} \div 1\frac{1}{2}$ 16. $2\frac{1}{3} \div 1\frac{5}{6}$

17. Copy and complete this multiplication grid.

$\times$	$\frac{1}{6}$		
$1\frac{1}{2}$	4		
	$\frac{3}{8}$		
		$2\frac{1}{25}$	
$\frac{3}{4}$		$\frac{9}{20}$	$\frac{2}{3}$

1. Mark sells 288 raffle tickets. Penny sells $3\frac{2}{3}$ times as many raffle tickets as Mark. How many tickets does Penny sell?

2. There are loads of identical pizzas at a party.

   Dave ate $\frac{1}{3}$ of a pizza and $\frac{4}{9}$ of another pizza.

   Simone ate $\frac{2}{9}$ of a pizza then $\frac{1}{3}$ of another and then $\frac{2}{5}$ of another.

   Sinan ate $\frac{2}{3}$ of a pizza and $\frac{7}{15}$ of another. Who ate the most pizza?

3. If seven tenths of a number is 42, what is three quarters of the number?

4. Kai spends $\frac{1}{5}$ of his money on travel and spends two thirds of the remaining money on food. What fraction of his money is left over?

5 Copy and complete

$$\frac{\square}{\square} \times \left(\frac{3}{5} + \frac{1}{4}\right) - \frac{1}{4} = \frac{11}{160}$$

6 The reciprocal of x is $\frac{1}{x}$.

(a) Find the reciprocal of the reciprocal of $\frac{5}{7}$.

(b) Find the reciprocal of (the reciprocal of 5 plus the reciprocal of 6).

7 A bath is $\frac{1}{3}$ full of water. The bath is $\frac{3}{4}$ full when a further 260 litres of water have been added. How many litres of water are in the bath now?

8 Work out

(a) $\dfrac{\left(\frac{1}{2} - \frac{1}{3}\right) \times \left(\frac{1}{4} - \frac{1}{5}\right)}{\frac{1}{2} + \frac{1}{3} + \frac{1}{4} + \frac{1}{5}}$

(b) $\sqrt[3]{\left(\frac{1}{4} + \frac{1}{8} + \frac{1}{32} + \frac{1}{64}\right)}$

9 At 7 p.m. a hall is $\frac{1}{10}$ full. A further 504 people enter the hall by 8 p.m. The hall is now $\frac{5}{8}$ full. How many people will be in the hall when it is completely full?

HWK 3E ——————————————————————————— **Main Book Page 61**

1 Copy and complete to change 0.17171717…. to a fraction.

Let r = 0.17171717…

100r = $\boxed{}$

99r = $\boxed{}$

r = $\dfrac{\boxed{}}{\boxed{}}$

In questions **2** to **7** change the recurring decimals to fractions.

2 0.8888….   **3** 0.232323….   **4** $0.\dot{6}\dot{2}$ **5** 0.304304304….   **6** $0.3\dot{3}\dot{6}$ **7** $0.\dot{5}\dot{4}$

8 Change these fractions to recurring decimals.

(a) $\frac{5}{6}$ (b) $\frac{3}{7}$ (c) $\frac{7}{13}$

HWK 4M/4E ——————————————————————————— **Main Book Page 62**

Write as a single fraction.

1 $\frac{1}{2}m + \frac{1}{3}m$ **2** $\frac{3}{5}x - \frac{1}{10}x$ **3** $\frac{x}{6} + \frac{x}{5}$ **4** $\frac{n}{4} \times \frac{n}{5}$

5 $\frac{2n}{5} - \frac{3n}{10}$ **6** $\left(\frac{m}{5}\right)^2$ **7** $\frac{5n}{6} \div \frac{1}{4}$ **8** $\frac{1}{3}n \times \frac{1}{5}n$

9 $\dfrac{4x}{7}+\dfrac{x}{3}$

10 $\dfrac{5}{x}\times\dfrac{4}{x}$

11 $\dfrac{9m}{10}\times\dfrac{2}{3}$

12 $\dfrac{5}{x}+\dfrac{7}{x}$

13 $\dfrac{5m}{8}\div\dfrac{m}{4}$

14 $\dfrac{9}{n}-\dfrac{4}{n}$

15 $\dfrac{4x}{5}\times\dfrac{3x}{4}$

16 Match up each question to the correct answer below.

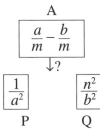

      A

$$\boxed{\dfrac{a}{m}-\dfrac{b}{m}}$$

$\downarrow?$

$$\boxed{\dfrac{1}{a^2}}\quad\boxed{\dfrac{n^2}{b^2}}$$

  P   Q

      B

$$\boxed{\dfrac{n}{ab}\div\dfrac{an}{b}}$$

$\downarrow?$

$$\boxed{\dfrac{a-b}{m}}$$

    R

      C

$$\boxed{\dfrac{2m}{3mn}\times\dfrac{n^2}{4n}}$$

$\downarrow?$

$$\boxed{\dfrac{1}{6}}\quad\boxed{\dfrac{ab}{m^2}}$$

  S   T

Rewrite the following as single fractions.

17 $\dfrac{3}{2x}+\dfrac{4}{x}$

18 $\dfrac{5mn^2}{n}\times\dfrac{3n}{m}$

19 $\dfrac{\pi r^2 h}{3r}\times\dfrac{h}{2\pi}$

20 $\left(\dfrac{n}{4}\right)^2\times\dfrac{3m}{n}$

21 $\dfrac{5r^2}{4n}\div\dfrac{15n}{2r}$

22 $\dfrac{m}{n}+\dfrac{n}{m}$

HWK 5M/5E   **Main Book Page 64**

Solve the equations.

1 $\dfrac{x}{6}=-3$

2 $5=\dfrac{x}{7}$

3 $\dfrac{5}{x}=8$

4 $\dfrac{3x}{5}=6$

5 $\dfrac{5x}{9}=4$

6 $4=\dfrac{1}{x}$

7 $\dfrac{7}{x}=\dfrac{2}{3}$

8 $\dfrac{-3}{4}=\dfrac{15}{x}$

Now solve these.

9 $\dfrac{x}{2}+5=8$

10 $\dfrac{x}{4}-3=7$

11 $4+\dfrac{x}{5}=11$

12 $\dfrac{1}{3}x-6=8$

13 $\dfrac{1}{5}x+3=10$

14 $\dfrac{3}{5}x-6=1$

15 $\dfrac{5}{6}x+2=13$

16 $9+\dfrac{3x}{7}=14$

Finally solve these equations.

17 $\dfrac{5}{x}=\dfrac{3}{x+1}$

18 $\dfrac{10}{3x-1}=2$

19 $\dfrac{x+4}{2}=\dfrac{5x-2}{3}$

20 $\dfrac{6}{2-x}=4$

21 $\dfrac{4}{x+3}-2=0$

22 $\dfrac{4(x+1)}{5}=\dfrac{3(x-2)}{4}$

2.2 Working with indices

HWK 1M   **Main Book Page 65**

Write each answer in index form.

1 $5\times5\times5\times4\times4\times4\times4$

2 $a\times a\times a\times a$

3 $4^6\times4^2$

4 $7^6\times7^{10}$

5 $10^7\times10^4$

6 $n^5\times n^3$

7 $x^6 \div x^2$

8 $a^{10} \div a^5$

9 $6^{12} \div 6^4$

10 $n^8 \div n$

11 $x^{16} \div x^7$

12 $m^6 \times m$

13 Answer true or false:

(a) $4^2 \times 4^3 = 4^6$

(b) $2^8 \div 2^3 = 2^5$

(c) $5^{10} \div 5^5 = 5^2$

(d) $8^4 \div 8^3 = 8$

(e) $9^{12} \div 9 = 9^{11}$

(f) $6^8 \div 6^4 = 6^4$

14 Work out and write each answer in index form.

(a) $\dfrac{6^4 \times 6^3}{6^5}$

(b) $\dfrac{5^4 \times 5^6}{5^3}$

(c) $\dfrac{2^5 \times 2^3 \times 2^2}{2^4 \times 2^4}$

(d) $\dfrac{m^6 \times m^3}{m^4}$

(e) $\dfrac{n^5 \times n^3 \times n^6}{n^7 \times n^2}$

(f) $\dfrac{m^{10}}{m^3 \times m}$

15 Which is the larger answer and by how much?

$$\frac{2^4 \times 2^5}{2^6}$$

P

or

$$\frac{2^3 \times 2^7 \times 2^4}{2^6 \times 2^6}$$

Q

16 $\dfrac{3^7 \times \square \times 3^4}{3^8} = 3^7$ Write down the number which belongs in the empty box.

17 $\dfrac{7^6 \times 7^4 \times 7^7}{7^3 \times \square} = 7^8$ Write down the number which belongs in the empty box.

HWK 1E   **Main Book Page 66**

Remember: $x^{-n} = \dfrac{1}{x^n}$

Write the answer as an ordinary number.

1 5^{-2}

2 10^{-2}

3 3^{-1}

4 2^{-4}

5 4^{-3}

6 $7^2 \times 7^{-4}$

7 $2^{-6} \times 2^3$

8 $3^{-8} \times 3^5$

In questions **9** to **17**, answer true or false.

9 $n^{-2} = \dfrac{2}{n}$

10 $\dfrac{n^2}{n^3} = n^{-1}$

11 $x^{-2} \times x = \dfrac{1}{x}$

12 $\dfrac{x^2}{x^4} = \dfrac{1}{x^2}$

13 $a^{-3} = \dfrac{1}{a^3}$

14 $n^2 \times \dfrac{1}{n^4} = n^{-2}$

15 $10^3 \div 10^6 = -30$

16 $n^{-5} = \dfrac{1}{n^5}$

17 $3x^{-2} = \dfrac{1}{3x^2}$

In questions **18** to **23**, copy and complete.

18 $3^2 \times \square = 3^{-1}$

19 $1 \div 5^6 = \square$

20 $2 \div \square = \dfrac{1}{2^4}$

21 $7^4 \div \square = 7^7$

22 $\left(\dfrac{1}{3}\right)^3 \times \square = 3^{-1}$

23 $\left(\dfrac{1}{6}\right)^4 \div \square = 6^{-2}$

Main Book Page 67

1 Simplify

(a) $(m^3)^4$
(b) $(y^5)^2$
(c) $(n^6)^4$

2 Answer true or false:

(a) $(5^2)^3 = 5^5$
(b) $(3^4)^2 = 3^8$
(c) $(2^3)^2 \times 2^2 = 2^8$

(d) $(4^2)^4 = 4^6$
(e) $(7^3)^5 \div 7^{10} = 7^5$
(f) $(9^2)^2 \times (9^3)^2 = 9^{24}$

3 Work out and write each answer in index form.

(a) $\dfrac{(7^4)^3}{7^8}$
(b) $\dfrac{(3^5)^3}{3^{10}}$
(c) $(2^6)^3 \times 2^3$

(d) $\dfrac{9^{12}}{(9^3)^2}$
(e) $(4^4)^5 \times (4^3)^3$
(f) $\dfrac{(m^3)^4}{(m^2)^5}$

(g) $\dfrac{(n^4)^5 \times n^7}{n^{16}}$
(h) $\dfrac{m^6 \times (m^3)^3}{(m^2)^6}$
(i) $\dfrac{(n^4)^4 \times (n^2)^6}{(n^5)^5}$

4 Give each final answer as an ordinary number.

(a) $3 \times (3^2)^2$
(b) $\dfrac{(5^2)^6 \times 5^4}{(5^5)^3}$
(c) $\dfrac{(7^4)^3}{(7^2)^5}$

(d) $\dfrac{6^4 \times 6^6}{(6^4)^2}$
(e) $\dfrac{(2^3)^3 \times (2^4)^2}{(2^7)^2}$
(f) $\dfrac{(4^3)^6}{(4^4)^3 \times (4^2)^2}$

5 Simplify

$$\frac{(3^5)^4 \times (3^2)^3 \times 3^9}{(3^2)^7 \times 3^5 \times (3^4)^2}$$

6 *Explain* why 3^0 is equal to 7^0.

7 Work out the actual value of

$$\frac{(2^6)^2 \times 2^4 \times 2^0 \times (2^{-3})^3}{2^2 \times (2^{-2})^2}$$

Main Book Page 68

Solve the equations for n.

1 $n^3 = 64$
2 $3^n = 81$
3 $5^n = 125$
4 $5^n = \dfrac{1}{25}$
5 $7^n = 1$

6 $8^n = \dfrac{1}{8}$
7 $3^n \times 3^2 = 27$
8 $\dfrac{10^n}{10^4} = \dfrac{1}{10}$
9 $2^{n-3} = 16$
10 $4^{n+1} = \dfrac{1}{16}$

11 $2^5 \times 2^n = 8$
12 $\dfrac{5^2}{5^n} = \dfrac{1}{5}$

Use a calculator to evaluate the following.

13 3^6
14 $36^{1/2}$
15 7.12^0
16 $625^{0.5}$
17 2^{10}

18 $256^{0.25}$ **19** $100^{1/2}$ **20** $196^{0.5}$

21 Explain what the rule $x^{1/2}$ works out.

22 Explain what the rule $x^{1/3}$ works out. (Hint: test the numbers 1, 8, 27, 64 and 125)

HWK 3M/3E ———————————————————————— **Main Book Page 69**

In questions **1** to **6** give your answer in index form.

1 £10^7 is won by 100 people. How much money does each person get?

2 Work out the volume of this cube.

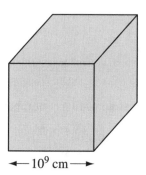

←— 10^9 cm —→

3 The distance from the Earth to the star, Nexus, is 10^{18} km. The star, Prontius, is one thousand times further away from the Earth. How far is Prontius from the Earth?

4 Find the volume of this triangular prism.

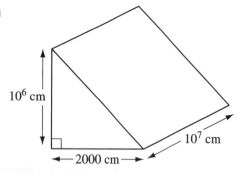

10^6 cm

10^7 cm

←— 2000 cm —→

5 There are 2^{10} tiles on a wall. Each tile has 8 leaves on it. How many leaves are there in total (give your answer as a power of 2)?

6 The volume of each cuboid is the same. Find the value of x.

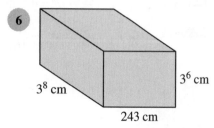

3^6 cm

3^8 cm

243 cm

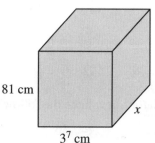

81 cm

x

3^7 cm

7 (a) Draw the graph of $y = 4^x$ for values of x from -2 to 4. Use a scale of 2 cm to 1 unit for x and 1 cm to 20 units for y.

(b) Use the graph to give an estimate for the value of x which satisfies the equation $4^x = 50$.

8 Solve the equations for x.

(a) $2^x + 3^x = 97$ (b) $x^2 + 4^x = 73$ (c) $5^x = 56$ (give your answer to 1 decimal place)

2.3 Standard form

| HWK 1M | Main Book Page 72 |

Write these numbers in standard form.

1 80000   **2** 650   **3** 3400   **4** 0.048   **5** 7340000   **6** 7 million

7 26   **8** 0.000314   **9** 238 million   **10** 0.000053   **11** 0.7   **12** 4183

13 0.019   **14** 36 million   **15** 0.009   **16** 3824500

Write the following as decimal numbers.

17 3×10^{-3} **18** 7×10^2 **19** 3.9×10^{-1} **20** 5.36×10^6

21 1.74×10^5 **22** 2.4×10^{-4} **23** 1.86×10^{-5} **24** 4.816×10^4

25 The area of a country is 7.8×10^4 km². Write this number in decimal form.

26 The annual budget for a large secondary school is £7×10^6. Write this in decimal form.

27 The speed of light is 3×10^8 m/s. Write this in decimal form.

28 An atom has a mass of 0.000 000 000 000 000 000 00019 grams. Write this in standard form.

29 The Government has to reduce its spending this year by 6 thousand million pounds. Write this number in standard form.

30 47384 people watch a football match. Write this in standard form.

| HWK 1E | Main Book Page 73 |

1 If the number 5.237×10^{10} is written out in full, how many zeros follow the 7?

2 Find the area of this shape in cm², giving your answer in standard form.

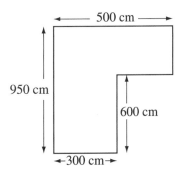

3 A snail moves 36 m in 200 hours. Find the average speed of the snail in cm/s, giving your answer in standard form.

4 Write the number below in order of size, smallest first:

| A | 3×10^6 | B | 2×10^{-7} | C | 40000 | D | 5×10^{-3} | E | 4×10^6 |

5 During the year 2009, a rock star earns 48p each second. How much does the rock star earn in 2009, giving the answer in standard form.

6 A crate weighs 75 kg. How many grams will 3200 crates weigh? Give your answer in standard form.

7 $x = 3 \times 10^4$ and $y = 2 \times 10^5$

Work out the following, giving your answers in standard form.

(a) xy (b) $10y$ (c) $\dfrac{x}{100}$ (d) $x + y$

8 If V = IR, find the value of V if I = 0.2 and R = 10^4. Give the answer in standard form.

9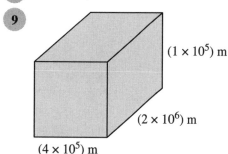
(1×10^5) m

(2×10^6) m

(4×10^5) m

Find the volume of this cuboid, giving your answer in standard form.

10 Write down the next two numbers in the sequence:

2×10^2, 8×10^3, 3.2×10^5,   ☐ ,   ☐

HWK 2M/2E   **Main Book Page 75**

Use a calculator to work out the following and write the answer in standard form.

1 6000×3000 **2** 8300×6 million   **3** $(900000)^2$

4 $20000000 \div 800$ **5** $(3 \times 10^6) \times (5 \times 10^4)$ **6** $(7 \times 10^{-6}) \times (4 \times 10^{-9})$

7 $(5 \times 10^6) \div (2 \times 10^{-8})$ **8** $(3 \times 10^{-7}) \div (4 \times 10^{-15})$ **9** $(6 \times 10^8)^2$

10 $(1.8 \times 10^{-3}) \times (7 \times 10^{24})$ **11** $(4 \times 10^{-10}) \times (7 \times 10^{12})^2$ **12** $(8 \times 10^{26}) + (5 \times 10^{25})$

In questions **13** to **20**, give answers in standard form correct to 3 significant figures, where necessary.

13 1.28×10^6 people watch a new blockbuster movie at the cinema over a period of time. If, on average, they each pay £7.20, what is the total amount of money spent watching this movie?

14 Calculate the area of this triangle.

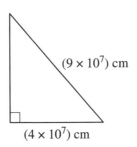

(9×10^7) cm

(4×10^7) cm

15 The distance of the Earth from the Sun is about 1.496×10^{11} m. The speed of light is 2.998×10^5 km/s. How long does it take the light from the Sun to reach the Earth?

16 An ill person has 4×10^8 viruses in his body. During the next 24 hours, the number of viruses increase by 98%. Work out the increase in the number of viruses during this 24 hour period.

17 10^{100} is called a googol. Work out the value of $(3.5 \text{ googols})^3$, giving your answer in standard form.

18

(5×10^{12}) cm

The area of the rectangle is equal to the area of the circle. Find the value of x.

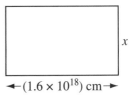

x

(1.6×10^{18}) cm

19 $v^2 = \dfrac{GM}{r}$ Find the value of v if $G = 1.7 \times 10^{-11}$, $M = 8 \times 10^{25}$ and $r = 7300\,000$.

20 One light year is 9.46×10^{12} km (the distance travelled by light in one year). A star is 3.7×10^6 light years from the Earth. What is the distance of this star from the Earth in km?

2.4 Applying mathematics in a range of contexts 1

HWK 1/2/3/4/5 ──────────────────────────────── **Main Book Page 78**

1 John writes down three consecutive whole numbers. Three times the smallest number plus three times the middle number equals 10 more than five times the largest number. Write down the three consecutive numbers.

2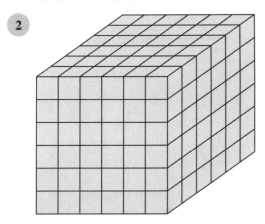

This $6 \times 6 \times 6$ cube is made from small cubes as shown. Each cube on the outside weighs 8g. Each cube on the inside weighs 5g. What is the total weight of this $6 \times 6 \times 6$ cube?

3 Work out $\dfrac{5^2}{8} \times \dfrac{2^3}{8^2} \times \dfrac{4^3}{5^3}$

4 Petra is planning to throw a big party. She wants to provide good food with a waiter service. She needs 2 chefs, 3 waiters and one person to wash and clear up.

She knows 7 people who can do some of these jobs. They each charge different hourly rates, depending on which job they are doing. The table below provides all this information.

Name	Job	Hourly rate
Terry	Junior chef	£7
	Waiter 2	£6.80
Maggie	Waiter 1	£6.50
Simon	Waiter 1	£6.80
	Waiter 2	£6.50
Laura	Main chef	£9.15
	Junior chef	£7
	Washer	£8.25
Darryl	Main chef	£9.20
Buffy	Main waiter	£9
Reece	Junior chef	£7.50
	Main waiter	£9.20

Petra needs to choose 6 people only to do the 6 jobs (Main waiter, waiter 1, waiter 2, washer, Main chef and Junior chef). They will each work for 8 hours and Petra needs to spend the least amount of money possible. Who should Petra choose for each job and how much will she pay in total for the 8 hours?

Show all your working out clearly.

5 A chef has some pastry in the shape of a 4 cm × 6 cm × 12 cm cuboid. The chef rolls out the pastry so that it has a circular area of diameter 25 cm. Assuming that this area is a perfect circle, what will be the thickness of this pastry?

2.5 Scatter graphs

HWK 1M/1E ——————————————————————— **Main Book Page 85**

1 Match one statement from the top of the next page to each scatter graph below to describe the correlation.

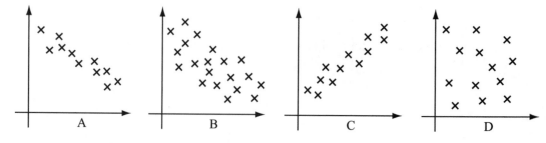

1	strong positive correlation

2	strong negative correlation

3	weak positive correlation

4	weak negative correlation

5	no correlation

2 The scatter graph below shows the heights of some people and their corresponding foot lengths.

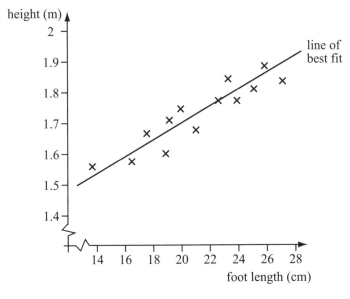

(a) Describe the correlation.

(b) Estimate the height of a person with a foot length of 14 cm.

(c) Estimate the foot length of a person of height 1.76 m.

3 The table below shows the marks obtained by some students in a calculator and a non-calculator maths test.

calculator	54	70	86	60	90	50	76	40	96	66	80
non-calculator	50	60	80	70	72	60	70	54	78	54	76

(a) Plot this data on a scatter graph with the calculator marks on the horizontal axis.

(b) Draw the line of best fit.

(c) Estimate the non-calculator mark of a student who get 56 in the calculator test.

(d) Estimate the calculator mark of a student who got 76 in the non-calculator test.

4 The table below shows the daily hours of sunshine and the daily anount of rainfall over a two week period for a Pacific island.

sunshine (h)	10	5.5	7.5	16	6	1	11	12	2	4	12.5	1	13	9
rainfall (mm)	14	26	21	10	21	34	20	14	26	30	10	29	15	17

(a) Plot this data on a scatter graph, with the hours of sunshine on the horizontal axis.

(b) Estimate the hours of rainfall on a day when there are 8 hours of sunshine.

2.6 Trial and improvement

1 The length of the rectangle is four times the width. Try different numbers until you find the dimensions that give the correct area.

$$\text{area} = 12.96 \text{ cm}^2$$

2

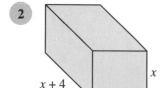

The volume of the box is given by the formula $x(x + 2)(x + 4)$. The box has a volume of 1287 cm^3. Find the dimensions of the box.

$x + 4$

$x + 2$

x

3 Find the value of x for each rectangle. Give your answer in the form: 'x is between _____ and _____ ', where the two numbers to be found differ by 0.1.

(a)

area = 40 cm^2 x

$x + 5$

(b)

area = 66 cm^2 $x - 1$

x

4 Solve the equations below. Give your answers in the form 'x is between _____ and _____ ', where the two numbers to be found differ by 0.1.

(a) $x(x + 7) = 150$ (b) $x^2 - 4x = 11$

1 Use trial and improvement for each rectangle below to find the value of x to 1 decimal place.

(a)

area = 42 cm^2 | x

$x + 4$

(b)

area = 31 cm^2 | x

$x + 6$

2 A rectangular room has an area of 58 m^2. The length of the room is 4.5 m greater than the width of the room. Find the width of the room correct to one decimal place.

3 Use trial and improvement to solve the equations, correct to 1 decimal place.

(a) $x^2 - x = 69$ (b) $x^2 + 3x = 43$ (c) $x(x - 4) = 27$

4

$x + 1$

$x + 2$ x

The volume of this cuboid is 143 cm^3.
Use trial and improvement to find the value of x, correct to 1 decimal place.

5 The shaded area shown opposite is 419 cm^2.

Use trial and improvement to find the value of x, correct to 1 decimal place.

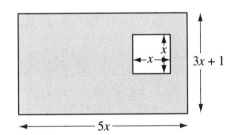

x

x

$3x + 1$

$5x$

1

2.8 cm

$x + 1$

x

Find the value of x, correct to 1 decimal place.

2 The total area of this shape is 214 cm^2. Find the value of the radius, r, correct to 1 decimal place.

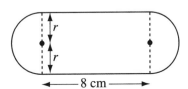

r

r

8 cm

3 If $(x + 3)^5 = 7089$, find the value of x, correct to 2 decimal places.

4 Solve these equations, correct to 1 decimal place.

    (a) $5^x = 66$ (b) $16^x = 3$ (c) $x^x = 41$

5 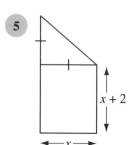 The total area of this shape is 120 cm². Find the value of x, correct to 1 decimal place.

$x + 2$

x

6 The area of circle P plus the area of circle Q is equal to the area of circle R. Find the value of x, correct to 1 decimal place.

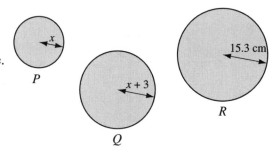

x

P

$x + 3$

Q

15.3 cm

R

7 Solve the equation $x^3 = 5\sqrt[3]{x}$, giving your answer correct to 2 decimal places.

8 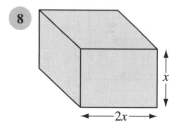 The volume of this cuboid is $10x^3$. Find the value of x, correct to 2 decimal places, if the total surface area is 588 cm².

x

$2x$

UNIT 3

3.1 Shape and space, mixed problems

HWK 1M — — — — — — — — — — — — — — — — — **Main Book Page 106**

Find the angles marked with letters.

1
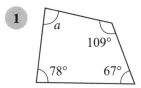
a
109°
78°   67°

2
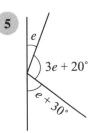
$4b$
b

3
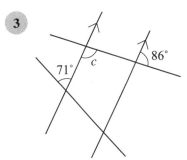
71° c 86°

4
10° d
45°

5
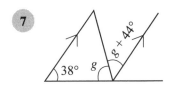
e
$3e + 20°$
$e + 30°$

6
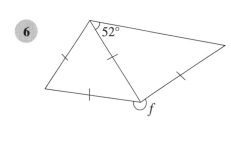
52°
f

7
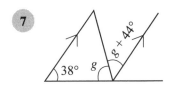
38° g
$g + 44°$

8
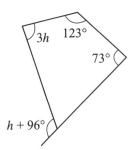
$3h$ 123°
73°
$h + 96°$

9
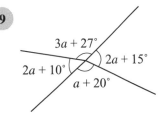
$3a + 27°$
$2a + 15°$
$2a + 10°$
$a + 20°$

10
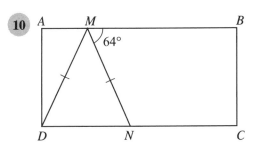
A M B
64°
D N C

ABCD is a rectangle. Triangle DMN is isosceles.
Find the value of AD̂M.

Remember: 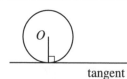   The angle between a tangent and radius is 90°.

tangent

Find the angles marked with letters.

1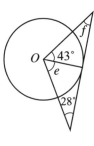

2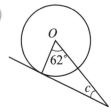

3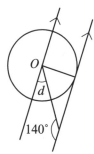

4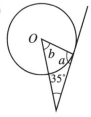

5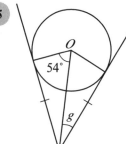

6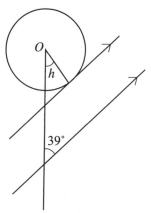

7 Draw a rectangle ABCD. Draw the two diagonals. M is the point of intersection of the two diagonals. DÂM = x°. Find AM̂D in terms of x.

8 Draw a triangle PQR with QP̂R = 90°. Point M lies on QR so that PM bisects QP̂R. PQ̂R = x°. Find PM̂Q in terms of x.

9 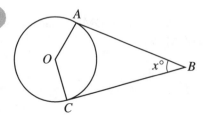   AB and BC are tangents to the circle. Find AÔC in terms of x.

Remember: Bearings are measured clockwise from North.

1 Find the bearings of:

(a) D from B

(b) C from E

(c) C from A

(d) B from C

(e) E from C

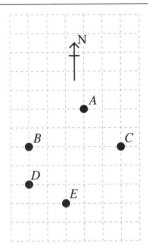

2 Mark a point A. Draw a point P which is 5 cm from A on a bearing of 205° from A.

3 Mark a point B. Draw a point P which is 6 cm from B on a bearing of 048° from B.

4

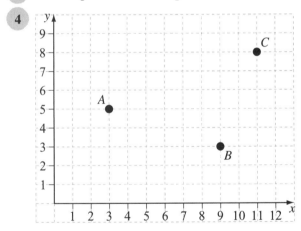

Write down the coordinates of the point which is:

(a) on a bearing 135° from A and 225° from B

(b) on a bearing 180° from A and 270° from B

(c) on a bearing 045° from A and 315° from B

(d) on a bearing 090° from A and 225° from C

(e) on a bearing 090° from B and 180° from C

5 A balloon flies 40 km on a bearing 126° and then a further 32 km on a bearing 035°. Make a scale drawing (1 cm = 8 km) and find how far the balloon is from its starting point.

6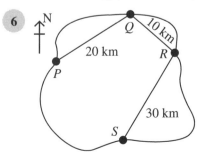

Q is on a bearing 060° from P.

R is on a bearing 150° from Q.

S is on a bearing 230° from R.

Make a scale drawing using 1 cm = 5 km.
How far is S from P and on what bearing is S from P?

44

Find the side marked x. All lengths are in cm. Give answers correct to one decimal place.

1

2

3

4
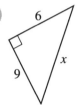

5
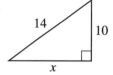

6
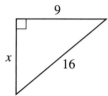

7

8
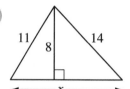

9
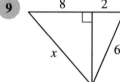

10 Two squares each of side length 4 cm are placed together as shown. Calculate the length AB.

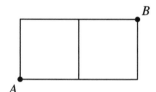

11 Calculate the value of x, correct to 2 decimal places.

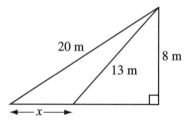

12
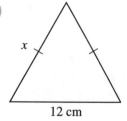

The area of this triangle is 45 cm². Calculate the value of x, correct to 2 decimal places.

1 Find the shaded area in each diagram. Lengths are in cm. Give your answers to 3 significant figures.

(a)

8

6

(b)

7

7

(c)

9

5

2 Find the total area of this shape. All arcs are semicircles. Give your answer to 3 significant figures.

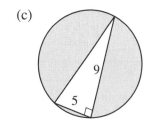

12 cm

── 10 cm ──

3

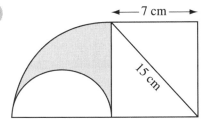

── 7 cm ──

15 cm

This diagram has one quarter circle, one semicircle and one rectangle. Calculate the shaded area. Give your answer to 3 significant figures.

1 Write down the equation of the mirror line for each reflection.

(a) ΔT → ΔW

(b) ΔR → ΔP

(c) ΔU → ΔR

(d) ΔQ → ΔS

(e) ΔV → ΔT

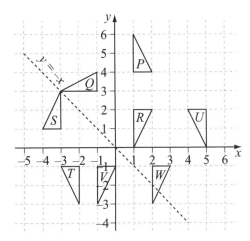

2 Copy the axes from question **1** and triangle Q only. Rotate triangle Q 90° clockwise about the origin (0, 0). (You may use tracing paper if you have any.)

46

3

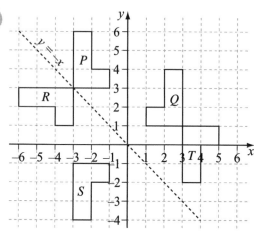

Describe fully each of the following transformations

(a) Q → T

(b) P → R

(c) S → P

4 (a) Draw axes with x and y from –6 to +6.

(b) Draw a rectangle with vertices at (–1, 2), (–4, 2), (–4, 3) and (–1, 3). Label this as shape A.

(c) Rotate shape A 90° clockwise about (0, 1). Label the new shape B.

(d) Reflect shape B in the line $y = x$. Label the new shape C.

5 Copy each shape with its centre of enlargement. Enlarge the shape by the scale factor given.

(a)

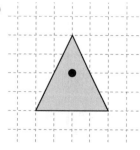

Scale factor 2

(b)

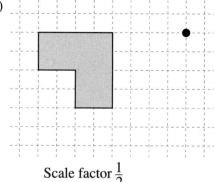

Scale factor $\frac{1}{2}$

(c)

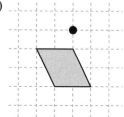

Scale factor $\frac{1}{2}$

(d)

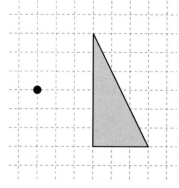

Scale factor $\frac{1}{3}$

6 Describe fully each of the following enlargements.

(a) Shape P → Shape Q

(b) Shape R → Shape S

(c) Shape Q → Shape P

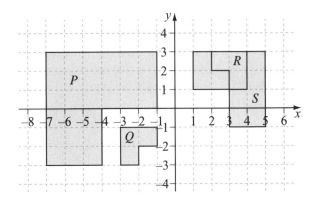

HWK 4E ───────────────────────────── **Main Book Page 113**

1 The bearing of A from B is 112°. What is the bearing of B from A?

2 Use a ruler, pencil and compasses *only* to construct an equilateral triangle with the side length 7 cm.

3 Use a ruler, pencil and compasses *only* to construct this triangle. Show your construction marks.

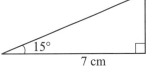

4 Mark walks on a bearing 134° for 5 km and then on a bearing 068° for 3 km. Make a scale drawing and then write down how far Mark is from his starting point.

5

1 kg ≈ 2.2 pounds	1 foot ≈ 30 cm
1 gallon ≈ 4.5 litres	1 km ≈ $\frac{5}{8}$ mile

Copy and complete

(a) 56 km ≈ ☐ miles

(b) 22.5 litres ≈ ☐ gallons

(c) $\frac{1}{2}$ foot ≈ ☐ mm

(d) 1500 g ≈ ☐ pounds

(e) 44 pounds ≈ ☐ kg

(f) 500 m ≈ ☐ mile

6 Two babies are weighed. Darryl weighs 8 pounds and Meryl weighs 3.5 kg. Which baby is heavier and by how much?

7

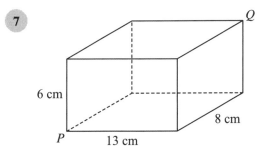

Use Pythagoras more than once to find the length of the diagonal PQ in the cuboid opposite. Give your answer to 1 decimal place.

8 The length of the diagonal AB of a cube is 10 cm. Calculate the length *x* of one side of the cube, giving your answer to 2 decimal places.

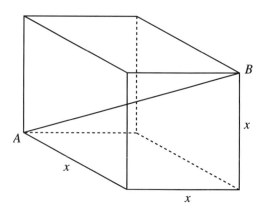

3.2 Sequences – finding a rule

HWK 1M/1E — Main Book Page 115

1 Look at the tables below. In each case, find a formula connecting the two letters in the form '*t* = …'

(a)

n	*t*
1	7
2	9
3	11
4	13
5	15

(b)

n	*t*
1	5
2	11
3	17
4	23
5	29

(c)

n	*t*
1	8
2	13
3	18
4	23
5	28

(d)

n	*t*
1	3
2	12
3	21
4	30
5	39

(e)

n	*t*
1	9
2	17
3	25
4	33
5	41

2 Write down each sequence in a table and then find the *n*th term.

(a) 3, 13, 23, 33, …

(b) 9, 13, 17, 21, …

(c) 5, 13, 21, 29, …

3 Find the *n*th term of each sequence below:

(a) 11, 17, 23, 29, …

(b) 1, 6, 11, 16, …

(c) 17, 14, 11, 8, …

4 Here is a sequence of shapes made from a number of matches m.

 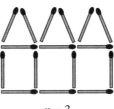

n	m
1	6
2	11
3	16
4	

$n = 1$ $n = 2$ $n = 3$
$m = 6$ $m = 11$ $m = 16$

Draw the next diagram in the sequence and write the values for n and m in a table.
How many matches are in the nth term?

5 Repeat question **4** for the sequence of shapes shown below.

 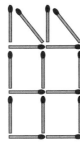 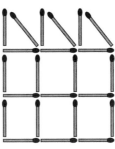

$n = 1$ $n = 2$ $n = 3$

6 Pam is putting up a fence. Each extra section is added as shown below. n stands for the number of sections.

  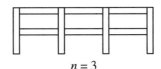

$n = 1$ $n = 2$ $n = 3$

(a) Complete the table where p is how many pieces of wood are used.

(b) Find an expression for how many pieces of wood are used for n sections of the fence.

(c) How many pieces of wood are used for 24 sections of the fence?

n	p
1	4
2	
3	
4	

7 Shapes are drawn on rectangular 'dotty' paper. The diagram number of the shape is recorded together with the total number of dots d on each shape.

$n = 1$

$n = 2$

$n = 3$

n	d
1	7
2	
3	
4	

(a) How many dots are there on the nth shape in the sequence?

(b) Which shape in the sequence will have 55 dots?

1 nth term $n^2 + 7n + 1$

Write down the first 5 terms of this sequence.

2 (a) nth term $= n^2 + 6n - 3$

Write down the first six terms of this sequence.

(b) Write down the difference between each pair of terms. What pattern do you notice?

Remember for quadratic sequences:
nth term formula contains $2n^2$ if second difference $= 4$
nth term formula contains $3n^2$ if second difference $= 6$

Use second differences to help you find the nth term of these sequences.

3 5, 11, 21, 35, 53, ...

4 2, 11, 26, 47, 74, ...

5 8, 11, 16, 23, 32, ...

6 −1, 5, 15, 29, 47, ...

7 2, 14, 34, 62, 98, ...

8 6, 21, 46, 81, 126, ...

9 6, 24, 54, 96, 150, ...

10 9, 21, 41, 69, 105, ...

Remember: For any quadratic sequence, nth term $= an^2 + bn + c$

Find the nth term of each sequence below:

1 2, 6, 12, 20, 30, ...

2 1, 5, 11, 19, 29, ...

3 6, 13, 22, 33, 46, ...

4 3, 11, 21, 33, 47, ...

5 1, 6, 15, 28, 45, ...

6 5, 16, 33, 56, 85, ...

7 9, 19, 33, 51, 73, ...

8 3, 15, 37, 69, 111, ...

9 $1^3 + 2^3 + 3^3 + \ldots + n^3 = \dfrac{n^2}{4}(n+1)^2$

(a) Show that this formula works with $n = 4$.

(b) Use the formula to find the value of

$$1^3 + 2^3 + 3^3 + 4^3 + 5^3 + 6^3 + 7^3 + 8^3 + 9^3 + 10^3$$

3.3 Rounding, estimating, errors and bounds

1 s.f. means 'significant figures'. Write the following numbers to the degree of accuracy indicated.

(a) 15.81 (2 s.f.)   (b) 0.6932 (3 s.f.)   (c) 5275 (2 s.f.)

(d) 39487 (3 s.f.)   (e) 5649.8 (2 s.f.)   (f) 0.08563 (1 s.f.)

(g) 0.9587 (3 s.f.)   (h) 138.96 (1 s.f.)   (i) 516896 (3 s.f.)

(j) 517.69 (2 s.f.)   (k) 0.08653 (2 s.f.)   (l) 3256.92 (3 s.f.)

2 Work out the area of each shape below with a calculator. Write each answer correct to 3 significant figures.

(a)
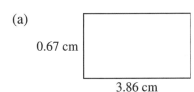
0.67 cm
3.86 cm

(b)
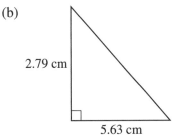
2.79 cm
5.63 cm

(c)
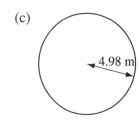
4.98 m

3 d.p. means 'decimal places'. Write the following numbers to the number of decimal places indicated.

(a) 8.79 (1 d.p.)   (b) 32.613 (2 d.p.)   (c) 0.3016 (2 d.p.)

(d) 16.147 (1 d.p.)   (e) 7.6138 (3 d.p.)   (f) 42.518 (1 d.p.)

4 Work out the following on a calculator and write the answers correct to two decimal places.

(a) $7.18^2 \times 3.6$ (b) $\dfrac{3.6}{2.7} + 0.517$ (c) $\dfrac{3.8^3}{2.3}$

(d) $\dfrac{8.36 + 4.128}{1.614}$ (e) $\dfrac{2.46}{\sqrt{3.49}}$ (f) $(7.63 - 1.94)^3$

5 The mean average number of people attending a Premiership football team's home games is 43514. If the team plays 19 home games in a season and each person pays £58.50 per game, how much money is paid in total? Give your answer to 3 significant figures.

Write down each calculation and decide (by estimating) which answer is closest to the exact answer. Do not do the calculation exactly.

	Calculation	Answer A	Answer B	Answer C
1	10.16×19.73	200	50	400
2	$51.62 \div 4.89$	50	1	10
3	$596.1 \div 31.37$	5	20	200
4	40.9×69.3	700	5600	2800
5	8.8^2	80	65	160
6	$20.07 \times 0.98 \times 10.36$	100	400	200
7	49% of 3016	150	1500	15000
8	$\sqrt{15.8} \times 9.83$	40	20	100
9	0.94% of £312	£310	£31	£3
10	$18.174 + 301.6 + 11.68$	325	330	340
11	$\dfrac{3.01 + 46.8}{10.17}$	7	100	5
12	$\frac{3}{5}$ of (31.3×49.18)	90	400	900
13	$\sqrt{99} \div \sqrt{3.899}$	5	2.5	30
14	$(198 - 151.36) \times 19.6$	100	1000	600
15	$\dfrac{6.99^2 + 19.65}{0.52}$	90	140	35
16	$0.99 \times 1.04 \times 0.97$	3	1	0.5
17	24.8% of $10^2 \times 101.6$	100	2500	250
18	$\sqrt{1596.85}$	400	40	50
19	$3.94^3 \times 48.16$	2500	3500	3000
20	$\frac{1}{5}$ of $\frac{1}{4}$ of 4.92×10^4	10	2500	1500

|

1. Tyrone works for half a year at a holiday resort. He earns £390 each week. Roughly how much does he earn in total?

2. 17890 people work for the local Council. During one year the Council reduces its work force by approximately 7%. Roughly how many people lose their jobs?

3. 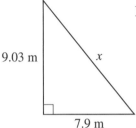 Estimate the value of x.

9.03 m

x

7.9 m

4. Carol leaves home at 09.15h and arrives at her sister's house at 13:09h. She travels at an average speed of 68.6 mph. Roughly how far is it from Carol's home to her sister's house?

5. There are nine calculations and nine answers below. Write down each calculation and choose the correct answer from the list given.

   (a) 2.1×19.8 (b) 82.1×3.9 (c) $47.38 \div 4$

   (d) 4.9×4.8 (e) $31.08 \div 5$ (f) $2.12 + 7.83$

   (g) $68.92 \div 2$ (h) 11% of 560   (i) 52.1×0.98

Answers	23.52	61.6	11.845
	34.46	41.58	51.058
	9.95	6.216	320.19

6. Approximately how much does a 14 stone 4 pounds man weigh in kilograms?
   (1 pound ≈ 0.45 kg and 1 stone = 14 pounds)

7. Answer true or false for the following questions:

   (a) $6.16 \times 0.4 < 6.16$ (b) $3.08 \times 0.26 > 3.08$ (c) $5.3 \div 0.2 > 5.3$

   (d) $6.29 \div 0.18 < 6.29$ (e) $83 \div 1.57 < 83$ (f) $4.4 \times 3.83 > 4.4$

   (g) $7.36 \times 0.99 > 7.36$ (h) $10.6 \div 4.32 < 10.6$ (i) $7.54 \times 0.06 < 7.54$

   (j) $0.38^2 < 0.38$ (k) $5.19 \div 0.004 > 5.19$ (l) $(1.003)^3 < 1.003$

8. Give an estimate for each of the following calculations. Show your working.

   (a) $\dfrac{2.95^2 + 9.03^2}{0.104}$ (b) $\pi \times 0.49^2$ (c) $\dfrac{6.05 \times 28.998}{10.014}$

   (d) $\dfrac{2487.2 - 501.69}{46.13 + 4.04}$ (e) 19.3% of 19.82^2 (f) $\dfrac{1.92^2 \times 15.16}{0.498}$

1 The diameter of a plate is 22 cm to the nearest cm. Write down the lower bound for the diameter of the plate.

2 Ann weighs 68 kg to the nearest kg. Write down the upper bound for Ann's weight.

3 The middle finger on Sam's left hand is measured at 7.3 cm to the nearest 0.1 cm. What is the least possible length of Sam's middle finger?

4 Copy and complete the table opposite. The first statement is done for you.

Quantity	Measured as:	Possible values
volume V	7 cm³ to the nearest cm³	$6.5 \leq V < 7.5$
width W	3.6 m to the nearest 0.1 m	$\square \leq W < \square$
time T	8.9s to the nearest 0.1 s	$\square \leq T < \square$
height h	24 cm to the nearest cm	$\square \leq h < \square$
radius r	5.3 m to the nearest 0.1 m	$\square \leq r < \square$

5 Mandy's suitcase weighs 4.7 kg. Write down the lower and upper bounds for this weight.

6

9.4 cm

6.2 cm

The base and height of a triangle are measured to the nearest 0.1 cm, as shown.

(a) Write down the lower bound for the height.

(b) Write down the upper bound for the base.

7 The temperature is taken as being 21.82°C to two decimal places. What is the least possible actual temperature?

8 A census states that the population of the UK is 58 million people correct to two significant figures.

(a) Write down the lower bound for the population.

(b) Write down the upper bound for the population.

1 This rectangle measures 14 cm by 6 cm to the nearest centimetre.

14 cm

6 cm

(a) Write down the least possible length and width of the rectangle.

(b) Work out the least possible area of the rectangle.

2 A tile weighs 43 g, correct to the nearest gram. What is the greatest possible weight of 50 tiles?

3 The distance between two cities is 180 km, to the nearest 10 km. Which range correctly completes the statement below:

'The true distance between the two cities lies between'

A | 170 km and 190 km | B | 175 km and 185 km | C | 179.5 km and 180.5 km

4 Write down the lower bound and upper bound for each quantity shown in the table opposite.

Quantity	Measured as:
weight w	4.16 kg to 2 decimal places
diameter d	81.5 cm to 1 decimal place
mass m	60 g to nearest 10 g
height h	7.36 mm to 2 decimal places
time t	110s to nearest 10s

5 A tin of fish weighs 210 g, to the nearest gram. What is the least possible weight of 15 tins?

6 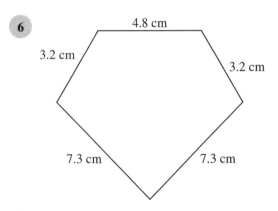 Each side of this pentagon has been measured to the nearest 0.1 cm. What is the actual lowest possible value for the perimeter of this pentagon?

7 V = IR is an electrical formula.

I = 7.6 to one decimal place.

R = 20.5 to one decimal place.

Calculate (a) the least possible value of V

(b) the greatest possible value of V

8 If $m = 9.4$, $n = 3.7$ and $p = 11.6$, all measured correct to one decimal place, calculate:

(a) the least possible value of $m + n$

(b) the least possible value of $m - n$

(c) the greatest possible value of $p - n$

9 If $w = 6.5$, $x = 9.2$ and $y = 0.8$, all measured correct to one decimal place, calculate:

(a) the greatest possible value of wxy

(b) the greatest possible value of $x - y$

(c) the least possible value of $w + x - y$

(d) the least possible value of $xy - w$

10 What is the greatest value (to one decimal place) of $A \div B$ if $A = 10.8$ and $B = 7.6$, each measured to one decimal place?

3.4 Drawing and visualising 3D shapes

HWK 1M/1E/2M ──────────────────────────── **Main Book Page 132**

1 Draw an accurate net for the triangular prism shown opposite.

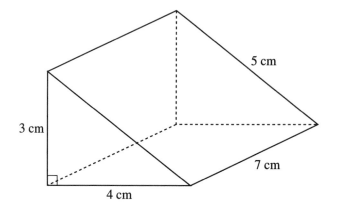

2 How many planes of symmetry does the triangular prism in question **1** have?

3 Draw an accurate net for the prism shown opposite.
All lengths are in cm.

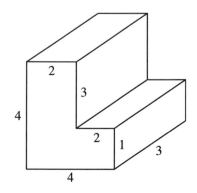

4

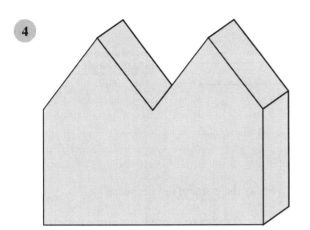

How many planes of symmetry does this solid have?

5 Draw a solid which has three planes of symmetry only.

6

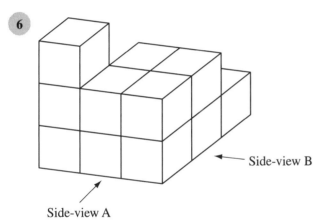

Side-view B

Side-view A

(a) Draw a diagram of side-view A.
(b) Draw a diagram of side-view B.

7 Draw a plan view and a side view of a cone.

8 The diagram shows a model made with 9 cubes, 3 grey and 6 white.

Draw 4 diagrams to show the side-views A, B, C and the plan view.

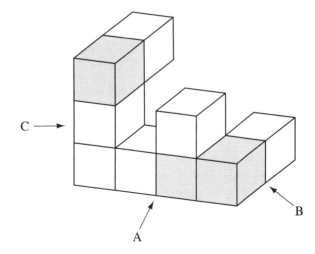

3.5 Percentage change

> Remember: % increase $= \left(\dfrac{\text{actual increase}}{\text{original value}}\right) \times 100$

Give answers correct to 1 decimal place, where necessary.

1. The price of a car drops from £7200 to £4200. What is the percentage decrease?

2. On average, Magnus gets 6 hours sleep each night. He decides to change his sleep pattern and manages to increase his sleep to 7 hours each night. What is the percentage increase in his hours of sleep each night?

3. Jerome buys a table for £190 and sells it for £250. Shania buys a sofa for £350 and sells it for £470. Who makes the larger percentage profit and by what percentage is it greater?

4. Find the percentage profit or loss for each item below.

camera	shirt	computer
cost price £60	cost price £32	cost price £380
selling price £81	selling price £25	selling price £550

5. Elouise buys a car for £8000. After 4 years the car is worth 60% less than this. Her cousin pays £500 more than this value for the car. Work out the percentage loss for Elouise.

6. Rory buys 80 cauliflowers at 55p each and sells them all for a total of £60. He also buys 75 cabbages at 45p each and sells 60 of them at 95p each. He has to throw away the remaining cabbages. Calculate Rory's overall percentage profit.

7.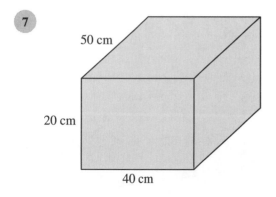

   (a) Work out the total surface area of this cuboid.

   (b) Each measurement is increased by 10%. Calculate the new total surface area of the cuboid.

   (c) What is the percentage increase in the surface area of the cuboid?

8 This chart shows the number of patients seen by a doctor in each of 4 weeks.

	Week 1	Week 2	Week 3	Week 4	Total
under 16	46	58	47	68	219
16 to 65	57	67	35	89	248
over 65	71	68	69	59	267
Total	174	193	151	216	734

(a) What was the percentage increase in the number of patients seen in week 4 compared to week 3?

(b) What was the percentage decrease in the number of under 16's seen in week 3 compared to week 2?

(c) What was the percentage increase in the number of 16 to 65 year old patients seen in week 4 compared to week 1?

9 A triangle has base 16 cm and height 9 cm. Calculate the percentage increase in the area of the triangle if the base is increased by 15% and the height is increased by 6%.

HWK 2M/2E	Main Book Page 142

You may use a calculator.

1 Zoe earns £33800 after a 4% pay increase. How much did she earn before the increase?

2 An investor loses 29% of his money on the Stock Market. He now has £227200 left.
How much money did he have before the loss?

3 Find the old price for each of the following items.

	Item	Old price	New price	% change
(a)	Shirt	?	£33.60	20% increase
(b)	Radio	?	£59.40	8% increase
(c)	Chair	?	£136	15% decrease
(d)	Table	?	£240.50	26% decrease
(e)	Skirt	?	£47.04	12% increase
(f)	Clock	?	£33.15	35% decrease

4 The number of people staying at hotels in the seaside resort of Barton in 2010 is 144336. This is a 7% decrease on the number in 2009 which was a 3% decrease on the number in 2008. How many people stayed at the hotels in 2008?

5 VAT (Value Added Tax) of 17.5% is added to the cost of a TV. The total cost is £752. How much does the TV cost before the VAT is added?

6 What is the cost of this camera without the VAT being included?
(VAT is 17.5%)

> Camera
>
> £242.05
> (including VAT)

7 Majid starts a new job. One year later he gets a 7% pay rise. Unfortunately one year after this he takes a 7% pay cut. This makes his salary £35226.54. How much was he paid when he started his new job?

8 A secondary school is expanding in size. It has 1386 pupils in September 2010. This was 10% more pupils than in September 2009 which was 5% more pupils than in September 2008. 53% of the pupils in September 2008 were boys. How many girls attended the school in September 2008?

| **HWK 3M/3E** | **Main Book Page 144** |

You may use a calculator.

1 Kelly writes a book. She has written 169 pages which is 65% of the pages that she eventually writes. How many pages are in the book when it is completed?

2 The number of road accidents in an area is 578 during one year. This is a 15% decrease compared to the previous year. How many road accidents were there during the previous year?

3

> Freeandeasy
>
> Cereal
>
> 13% fibre

A box of cereal contains 35.1 g of fibre.
What is the total weight of the box of cereal?

4 A gas bill is £39.69 which includes VAT at 5%. A unit of gas costs 9p before the VAT is added. How many units of gas were used to produce this bill?

5 The volume of a cone is worked

out by the formula $V = \frac{1}{3} \pi r^2 h$

where r is the radius of the
base and h is the perpendicular
height of the cone.

A cone has radius 4 cm and height 9 cm. A larger model of the cone is made with both the radius and height increased by 15%. Find the percentage increase in the volume of the cone.

6

rectangle	length	% increase in length	width	% increase in width
A	15 cm	8%	8 cm	9%
B	9 cm	10%	7 cm	7%
C	16 cm	7%	11 cm	9%
D	5 cm	12%	3.5 cm	5.5%

The four rectangles above are each increased by the percentage amounts shown. Work out the percentage increase in area for each rectangle. Write down the rectangles in the order of percentage increase in area, starting with the smallest.

7 A population of rabbits increases by 7% each year. In 2010 there are 8000 rabbits. How many rabbits will there be after:

(a) 1 year   (b) 2 years   (c) 5 years   (d) 20 years?

Give all your answers to the nearest whole number.

8 Bridget buys a car for £16000. Each year the car loses 18% of its value at the start of the year. How much is the car worth after   (a) 3 years   (b) 10 years?
Give your answers to the nearest penny.

9 Vijay puts £50000 in a bank. The annual interest rate is 8% (ie. each year the increase in money is 8% of the amount of money at the start of the year). After how many years will Vijay have reached £1 million in the bank?

UNIT 4

4.1 Transformations

> Remember: the translation vector $\begin{pmatrix} -4 \\ 2 \end{pmatrix}$ means the shape moves 4 units to the left and 2 units up

1

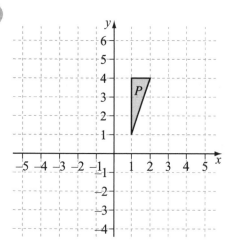

Copy this diagram.

(a) Translate shape P with the vector $\begin{pmatrix} -4 \\ -3 \end{pmatrix}$. Label the new shape Q.

(b) Translate shape P with the vector $\begin{pmatrix} 3 \\ -4 \end{pmatrix}$. Label the new shape R.

(c) Translate shape P with the vector $\begin{pmatrix} 2 \\ 2 \end{pmatrix}$. Label the new shape S.

(d) Write down the vector which will translate:

    (i)   shape Q onto shape R

    (ii) shape S onto shape Q

    (iii) shape R onto shape S

2   Look at the diagram opposite. Write down the vector for each of the following translations.

(a) A → E   (b) B → F

(c) F → E   (d) H → D

(e) B → G   (f) D → C

(g) C → G   (h) D → A

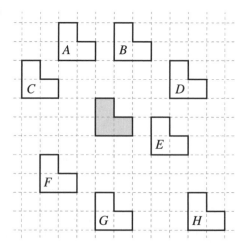

3   What vector is three times as long as and parallel to the vector $\begin{pmatrix} 2 \\ -6 \end{pmatrix}$?

4   Under a certain translation, the image of the point (4, –1) is (–2, 1). Find the image of the point (–2, 3) under the same translation.

5   What vector is four times as long as and opposite to the vector $\begin{pmatrix} -3 \\ 4 \end{pmatrix}$?

6   Under a certain translation, the image of the point (1, –3) is (4, –5). What point has (–1, 2) as its image under the same translation?

Tracing paper will be helpful in this exercise.

1 Describe *fully* each of the following
transformations:

(a) $\Delta A \rightarrow \Delta B$

(b) $\Delta C \rightarrow \Delta B$

(c) $\Delta E \rightarrow \Delta D$

(d) $\Delta C \rightarrow \Delta D$

(e) $\Delta E \rightarrow \Delta F$

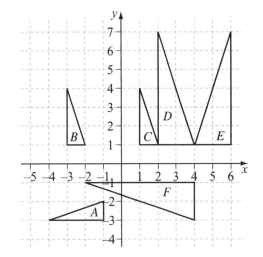

2 Find the image of the point (4, –2) after reflection in the line $y = -x$.

3 Find the image of the point (m, n) after reflection in the line $y = x$.

4 (a) Draw an *x*-axis from –8 to 5.

Draw a *y*-axis from –5 to 5.

(b) Draw a triangle with vertices at (3, 1), (3, 2) and (1, 2). Label this as triangle P.

(c) Enlarge triangle P by scale factor 2 about (3, 0). Label the new triangle Q.

(d) Reflect triangle Q in the line $x = -2$. Label the new triangle R.

(e) Translate triangle R with vector $\begin{pmatrix} 0 \\ -3 \end{pmatrix}$. Label the new triangle S.

(f) Rotate triangle S 90° anticlockwise about (–2, 1). Label the new triangle T.

(g) Rotate triangle T 90° clockwise about (0, –4). Label the new triangle U.

(h) Describe fully the transformation which maps triangle U onto triangle R.

64

1

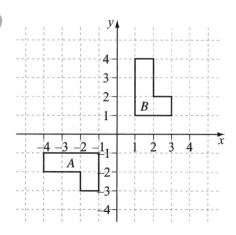

(a) Shape A is transformed into shape B by a reflection followed by a rotation about the origin. Describe these two transformations as fully as possible.

(b) Shape A can be mapped onto shape B by a *single* transformation. Describe this transformation as fully as possible.

2 (a) Shape A is transformed into shape B by a translation followed by a rotation about the origin. Describe these two transformations as fully as possible.

(b) Would the image be the same if the rotation was completed before the translation?

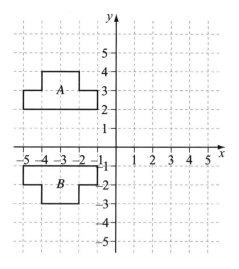

3 Draw axes for both x and y between -6 and $+6$.
Plot the points $(-1, 1)$, $(-5, 1)$, $(-5, 3)$ and $(-1, 3)$ then join them up to make a rectangle.

This is mapped onto the points $(1, 5)$, $(1, 1)$, $(3, 1)$ and $(3, 5)$ by two transformations: a reflection then a translation with $\binom{0}{n}$. Write down the axis of reflection and the value of n.

4 Copy the diagram shown opposite.
Three transformations are required to
map shape P onto shape Q, an enlargement
with centre (0, 4) followed by a rotation about
(0, 0) and lastly a translation. Describe these
transformations as fully as possible and
illustrate them on your diagram.

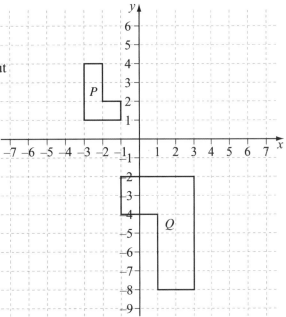

5 Draw an *x*-axis from –7 to 7 and a *y*-axis from –8 to 8. Plot the points (2, –1), (5, –7)
and (2, –7) then join them up to make a triangle.

This is mapped onto the points (–3, 2), (–1, 3) and (–1, 2) by two transformations:
an enlargement then a rotation about the origin. Describe these transformations as fully
as possible.

4.2 Reading and interpreting charts and graphs

HWK 1M/1E ────────────────────────────────── **Main Book Page 164**

1 240 people were asked to taste four different
flavoured ice creams. They were then asked
which was their favourite flavour. The results
are shown in the pie chart.

(a) How many people chose vanilla?

(b) How many people chose strawberry?

(c) How many more people chose chocolate than mint?

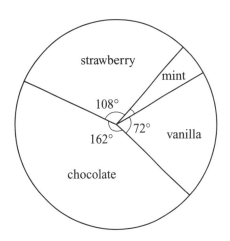

2 Three classes raise money for charity.

Jack says 'More children raised money for charity in class 9B than in class 9A'.

Is he correct or not? *Explain* your answer *fully*.

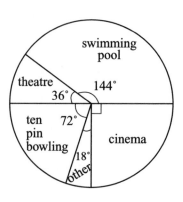

3

Job	Number of People
office	7
workshop	18
transport	12
sales	8

A small company has 45 people working for it.

Draw a pie chart to show the proportion of people working in each job as shown opposite.

4

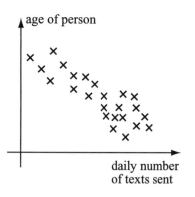

Describe briefly what this scatter graph shows.

5 120 people were asked what building for entertainment they would like to see built in Hexford. The results are shown opposite.

(Continued on the next page)

200 people were asked what building for entertainment they would like to see built in Atherton. The results are shown opposite.

(a) 'More people in Hexford than in Atherton want a swimming pool'. True or false? Give a clear reason for your answer.

(b) 'The same number of people in Hexford and Atherton want a cinema'. True or false? Give a clear reason for your answer.

HWK 2M/2E ———————————————————————— **Main Book Page 166**

1 The graph shows the amount of wine in a bottle during one evening. How many glasses of wine do you think were taken from the bottle?

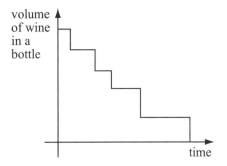

2 Which of the graphs A to D below best fits the following statement:
'The price of houses has been falling but increased slightly last month'.

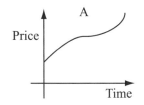 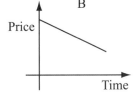 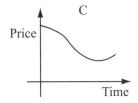 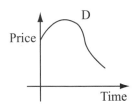

3 During the summer, the temperature increases until the middle of the afternoon then it becomes cooler. Draw a sketch graph to show the temperature during the day.

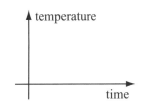

4 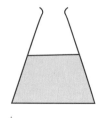 Water is poured into this container. Which of the graphs P to S below best shows how the water level would rise in the container?

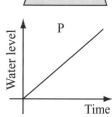 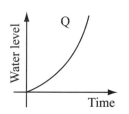 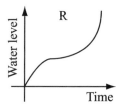 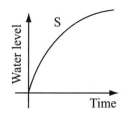

5 Tom saves money in a jar. He starts by putting £20 into the jar. At the end of every month he puts another £5 into the jar. Draw a sketch graph to show how much money is in the jar during the first six months of saving.

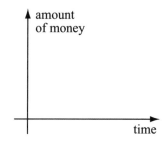

6 The graph opposite shows Amy's heart beat during one part of the day. Describe what Amy could be doing to produce this graph.

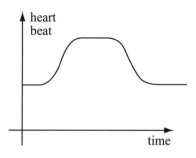

7 'The price of petrol has risen steadily over the last year but has stayed the same for the last two months'. Sketch a graph to illustrate this statement.

8 'Over the last year the cost of holidays to Spain has increased steadily but has started to fall over the last three months.' Sketch a graph to illustrate this statement.

9

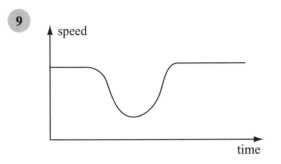

This graph shows the speed of a car during one part of a race. Describe what might be happening during this part of the race.

10 Terry buys a bag of jelly babies. He eats half of them very quickly then leaves the bag in his car for two days. He now heads off on a four hour journey in his car during which he gradually eats the remaining jelly babies. Draw a sketch graph to show the weight of jelly babies in the bag from when Terry buys the bag until the end of his car journey.

HWK 3M ──────────────────────────────────── **Main Book Page 169**

1

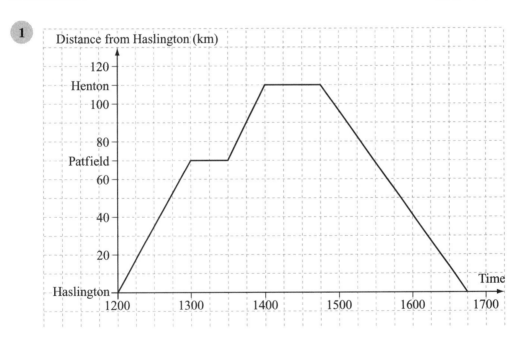

The graph above shows a car journey from Haslington to Henton and then back to Haslington.

(a) How far was the *total* journey?

(b) When did the car arrive back at Haslington?

(c) For how long did the car stop in Henton?

(d) Find the speed of the car

    (i) from Patfield to Henton

    (ii) from Henton back to Haslington

70

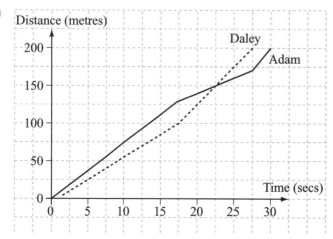

The graph above shows the performances of two runners during a 200 metres race.

(a) Who is winning after 10 seconds?

(b) At what time does Daley overtake Adam?

(c) Roughly how far behind Adam is Daley after 17.5 seconds?

(d) Who wins the race?

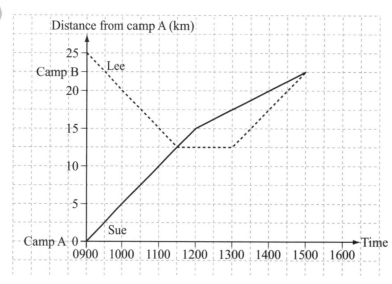

The graph above shows the walks of two hikers who start 25 km apart from each other.

(a) At what time do Lee and Sue first meet?

(b) For how long does Lee then stop for?

(c) How far ahead of Lee is Sue when Lee starts walking again?

(d) At what speed does Lee now walk in order to catch up with Sue?

4 (a) Draw a travel graph for the following journey.

'Tamsin leaves home at 1000. She walks at 6 km/h
for one hour then slows down to 4 km/h for
the next $\frac{1}{2}$ hour. She stops for 15 minutes then
walks for a further $1\frac{1}{2}$ hours at a speed of 6 km/h.
She has then arrived at a lake.'

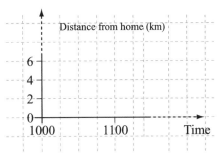

(b) Between what times did she stop for 15 minutes?

(c) At what time did she arrive at the lake?

(d) How far is the lake from Tamsin's home?

5 (a) Draw a travel graph for the following journey.

Fergus leaves home at 1300. He travels at 80 km/h for 45 minutes then stops
for $\frac{1}{2}$ hour. He then drives on a motorway for another $\frac{1}{2}$ hour at 120 km/h.

This gets him to an out of town shopping centre where he stays for one hour.
He then travels directly home at a speed of 80 km/h.

(b) At what time did he get to the shopping centre?

(c) How far is the shopping centre from his home?

(d) At what time did he get home?

4.3 Area and volume

HWK 1M ──────────────────────────────── **Main Book Page 172**

Remember: Volume of prism = area of cross-section × length

Area of trapezium = $\frac{1}{2}$h($a + b$)

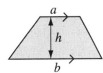

Give answers correct to 3 significant figures when necessary.

In questions **1** to **4** find the area of each shape. All arcs are either semi-circles or quarter circles and the units are cm.

1
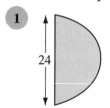
24

2
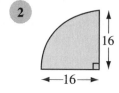
16
←16→

3
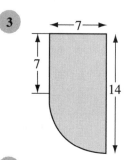
←7→
7
14

4
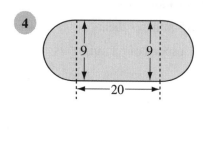
9   9
←20→

5 Find the total shaded area.
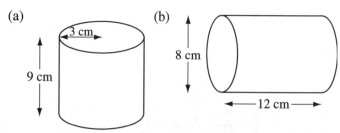
4 cm   9 cm
12 cm
←16 cm→

6
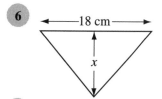
←18 cm→
x

The area of this triangle is 72 cm². Write down the value of length *x*.

7 Find the volume of each cylinder.

(a)
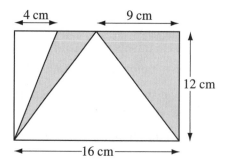
3 cm
9 cm

(b)
8 cm
←12 cm→

8 A stick of rock is a cylindrical shape. It has a radius of 1.9 cm. What is the length of the stick of rock if its volume is 295 cm³?

9

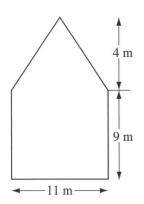

Shula paints one wall on the outside of her house as shown.

Each minute she paints 0.4 m². How long does it take her to paint the whole wall?

(Give your answer in hours and minutes)

10

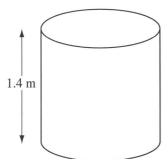

This container has diameter 0.92 m.

Calculate the capacity of the container in litres.

| HWK 1E | | Main Book Page 173 |

Give answers correct to 3 significant figures when necessary.

1 Find the total area of the shape below:

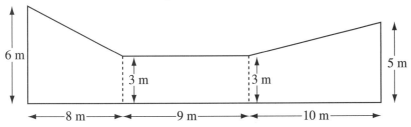

2 Find each shaded area. All lengths are in cm.

(a)

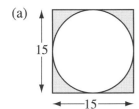

(b)

(c)

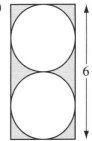

3 A trapezium has parallel sides of length 15 cm and 11 cm. Find the distance between the parallel sides if the area of the trapezium is 39 cm².

4

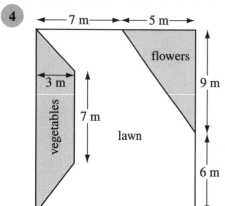

Calculate the area of the lawn in Mark's garden.

5 A cylindrical glass has diameter 9 cm and height 10 cm. A carton of juice in the shape of a cuboid measures 25 cm × 16 cm × 9 cm. How many times can the glass be completely filled with juice?

6

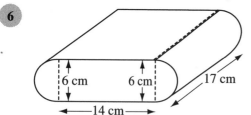

This diagram shows a case for binoculars. The front end is made from a rectangle and two semicircles as shown. Calculate the volume of this case.

7 Find the volume of a cube whose total surface area is 253.5 cm².

8 This container is filled with water at a rate of 200 ml per second. How long does it take to fill the tank completely? (Give your answer to the nearest minute)

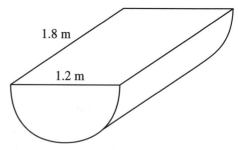

9 A machine component in the shape of a cuboid measures 12 cm × 8 cm × 2 cm. The entire component is covered with a protective substance which adds a thickness of 1 mm to each surface. Calculate the total volume of the protective substance used.

Give answers correct to 3 significant figures when necessary.

1 Find the radius of a circle with circumference of:

(a) 80 cm (b) 112 cm

2 Find the radius of a circle with area of:

(a) 58 cm² (b) 7.3 cm²

3 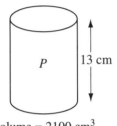 Which cylinder has the larger diameter and by how much?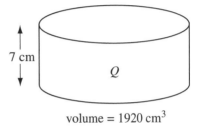

P | 13 cm

7 cm | Q

volume = 2100 cm³

volume = 1920 cm³

4 An iron bar measures 11 cm × 7 cm × 5 cm. It is melted down to make a cylinder of height 9 cm. Calculate the radius of the cylinder.

5 A cylindrical flagpole of height 8.6 m has volume 0.12 m³. What is the diameter of the flagpole?

6 Emma travels 6.42 km on her bike. The wheels on her bike rotate 3000 times. Find the diameter of the wheels.

7 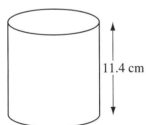 A cylindrical glass is completely filled with 808 ml of orange juice. What is the diameter of the glass?

(1 litre = 1000 ml = 1000 cm³)

11.4 cm

Give answers to 3 significant figures when necessary.

1 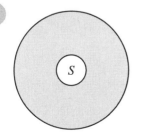 A circular staircase(s) is placed in the centre of a circular hall. The remaining floor area is carpeted. The diameter of the bottom of the circular staircase is 1.6 m. The area of the carpet used is 41.2 m². What is the diameter of the circular hall?

S

2

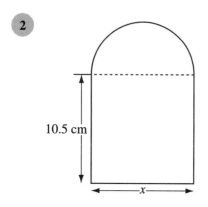

The perimeters of these 2 shapes are equal. Find the value of *x*.

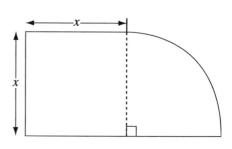

3 A circular boating lake contains 54 million litres of water. The depth of the water is consistently 1.3 m. What is the diameter of the boating lake?

4 A 2.5 litre pot of paint is 16 cm tall. Find the diameter of this pot of paint.

5

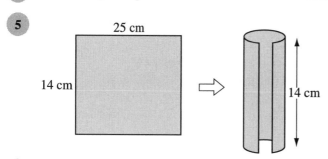

A rectangular piece of card is rolled up to make a tube (with no overlap). Find the diameter of the tube.

6 A cylinder contains 1.5 litres of water. How tall is the cylinder if its height is equal to its radius?

HWK 3M ─────────────────────────────── **Main Book Page 178**

Give answers to 3 significant figures when necessary.

1

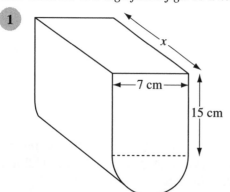

The volume of this prism is 2236 cm³.

Calculate the length *x*.

2 Find the missing lengths in the following prisms.

(a)

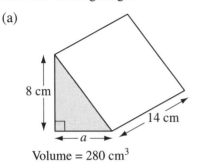

8 cm

14 cm

a

Volume = 280 cm³

(b)

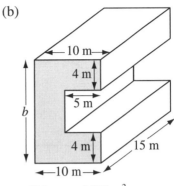

10 m

4 m

5 m

b

4 m

15 m

10 m

Volume = 1575 m³

3

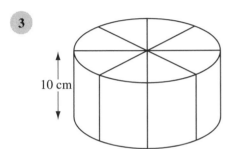

10 cm

A cake has a ribbon removed from its circumference then is cut into 8 equal slices. Each piece of cake has volume 660 cm³. What length of ribbon was needed to wrap exactly once around the circumference?

4 A cylinder of length 14 cm has volume 370 cm³. Will this cylinder fit inside a cuboid which measures 6 cm × 6 cm × 14.2 cm? You must show all your working out to justify your answer.

5 The capacity of this container is 23400 litres.
Calculate the length x.

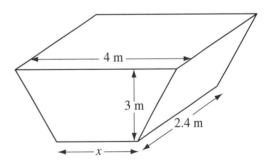

4 m

3 m

2.4 m

x

6 The heights of three cylindrical containers are in the ratio 1:3:4.
Their volumes are in the ratio 1:2:5.

The three containers are completely filled up using 12.5 litres of water.
Find the radius of each cylinder if the largest cylinder has height 36 cm.

7 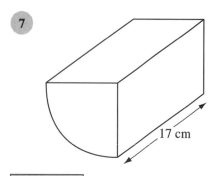 The cross-sectional area of this prism is a quarter circle. Calculate the total surface area of this prism if its volume is 1433 cm³.

17 cm

| **HWK 3E** | **Main Book Page 180** |

Give answers to 3 significant figures when necessary.

1 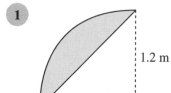 The shaded region represents a garden bed of soil. The bed of soil is 30 cm deep. Find the total volume of soil.

1.2 m

1.2 m

2 The shaded area opposite has an area of 48 cm². Find the length of a side of the square.

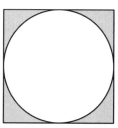

3 A box contains 64 cans of fruit. The diameter of each can is 8.5 cm. The box measures 50 cm by 34 cm by 34 cm. 13493 cm³ within the box is not occupied by the cans. Calculate the height of each can.

4 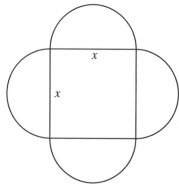 This shape is made from a square and four semi-circles. The total area is 140 cm². Calculate the value of x.

x

x

5 Write down an expression for the total surface area of this triangular prism in terms of a, b and c.

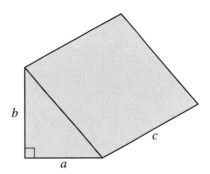

6 The area of this sector of a circle is 390 cm². Calculate the perimeter of this shape.

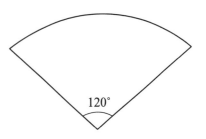

7 Cath is in a hurry one morning but needs to make a sandwich. She puts the slice of cheese shown below between two slices of bread.

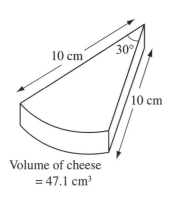

10 cm   30°

10 cm

Volume of cheese = 47.1 cm³

The plan view of a slice of bread is shown below.

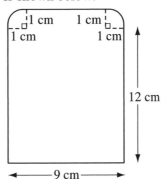

1 cm   1 cm
1 cm   1 cm

12 cm

9 cm

Assuming that the cheese and the slices of bread are prisms, calculate the total thickness of the sandwich if the volume of one slice of bread is double the volume of the cheese.

4.5 Applying mathematics in a range of contexts 2

| HWK 1/2/3/4/5 | Main Book Page 189 |

1 Find the 10th term and the 20th term of the sequence below:

1, 3, 7, 15, 31….

2 £3400 worth of pound coins occupy a volume of 4288 cm^3. The diameter of a pound coin is 2.24 cm. Calculate the thickness of one pound coin, giving your answer in mm correct to one decimal place.

3 Phil is trying to start his own business. He is producing resource packs about different countries which he wants to sell to schools, particularly nursery schools.

His costs and selling prices are shown below:

resource pack name	cost of raw materials (£)
Greece	2.46
Spain	2.73
India	4.15
U.S.A.	2.45
Australia	2.25
China	4.04
France	2.49

Phil must market his packs if he wants to sell as many as possible. Every 2 weeks he spends £83 on marketing.

Phil must pay insurance in case his packs lead to any accidents. This costs him £18.75 each week.

resource pack name	pack selling price (£)
Greece	7
Spain	7
India	9.50
U.S.A.	6.50
Australia	6
China	9.50
France	7

Phil works from home. The extra gas/electricity used costs him £15 weekly.

Profit from postage and package

Phil posts the packs to schools and charges extra for postage and package.

* if he sends 1 pack only, he makes £1.20 profit

* if he sends 2 packs together, he makes £1.60 profit

* if he sends 3 packs together, he makes £2 profit

Task

Once Phil's business is up and running, the number of sales of each pack during the first 4 weeks is shown below.

resource pack name	week 1	week 2	week 3	week 4
Greece	3	2	4	7
Spain	1	5	7	6
India	0	6	10	12
U.S.A.	1	3	5	6
Australia	2	7	3	5
China	1	6	10	15
France	0	4	6	5

The number of packs sent out together each week is shown below.

week 1	5 × 1 pack, 1 × 3 packs
week 2	4 × 1 pack, 7 × 2 packs, 5 × 3 packs
week 3	9 × 1 pack, 9 × 2 packs, 6 × 3 packs
week 4	15 × 1 pack, 10 × 2 packs, 7 × 3 packs

(a) Phil wants to make £140 profit per week on average during these 4 weeks.
Does he manage this? You must show all your working out. Remember the money he makes from the postage and package.

(b) Does the sales pattern suggest that Phil's business will be successful in the long term?
Explain your reasons for giving your answer.

4 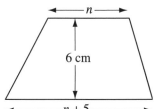 The area of the trapezium is equal to the area of the triangle. Find the value of n.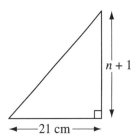

5 The speed of light is 3×10^8 m/s. Find the speed of light in km/h, giving your answer in standard form.

82

4.6 Simultaneous equations

1 Use the graph to solve
the simultaneous equations.

(a) $x + y = 4$
 $3x - y = 4$

(b) $x + y = 4$
 $x - y = -2$

(c) $3x - y = 4$
 $x - y = -2$

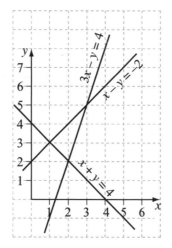

2

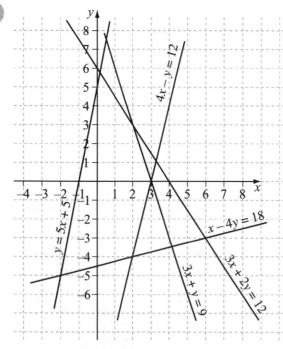

Use this graph to solve the
simultaneous equations.

(a) $4x - y = 12$
 $x - 4y = 18$

(b) $3x + 2y = 12$
 $3x + y = 9$

(c) $3x + 2y = 12$
 $x - 4y = 18$

(d) $3x + y = 9$
 $4x - y = 12$

(e) $x - 4y = 18$
 $y = 5x + 5$

HWK 1E ————————————————————————————————— **Main Book Page 198**

Solve these simultaneous equations by drawing straight line graphs first.

1 $x + y = 5$

$y = 2x - 1$

Draw axes with x and y from 0 to 6.

2 $x + 4y = 8$

$2x + y = 9$

Draw axes with x and y from 0 to 9.

3 $2x + 3y = 12$

$3x - y = 7$

Draw the x-axis from 0 to 8 and
the y-axis from –7 to 5.

4 $x - 2y = 10$

$3x + 2y = 6$

Draw the x-axis from 0 to 10 and the
y-axis from –6 to 4.

5 Consider the 3 equations: $2x - 3y = 16$

$5x + 2y = 2$

$5x + 2y = 16$

One pair of these equations would give no solutions, Which pair and why?
(Hint: think about their graphs)

HWK 2M/2E ————————————————————————————— **Main Book Page 200**

Solve the simultaneous equations.

1 $3x + y = 10$

$4x + y = 13$

2 $7x + 2y = 22$

$5x + 2y = 18$

3 $x + 4y = 14$

$x + 3y = 12$

4 $4x + 2y = 26$

$4x - y = 17$

5 $6x + y = 21$

$2x - y = 3$

6 $4x - 2y = 10$

$x + 2y = 0$

7 $3x + y = -1$

$2x + y = 1$

8 $2x + 3y = -1$

$4x - 3y = -29$

9 $x - 5y = 6$

$2x + 5y = -18$

10 $2x = y + 11$

$2x + 2y = 2$

11 $3x - 4y = 7$

$x = 5 - 4y$

12 $5x = 3y - 3$

$2x + 3y = -18$

HWK 3M/3E ————————————————————————————— **Main Book Page 201**

In questions **1** to **3** alter one of the equations and then solve the simultaneous equations.

1 $5x + 3y = 27$

$2x - y = 2$

2 $4x - 2y = 26$

$3x + y = 22$

3 $2x - 4y = -14$

$4x + y = 26$

In questions **4** to **15** alter both equations and then solve the simultaneous equations.

4 $3x + 2y = 16$

$2x + 5y = 29$

5 $2x + 6y = 18$

$5x - 4y = 7$

6 $7x - 3y = -5$

$5x + 4y = 21$

7 $5x + 3y = 46$

$2x + 7y = 30$

8 $7x - 5y = -41$
   $4x + 6y = 12$

9 $2x - 3y = -6$
   $5x - 2y = -26$

10 $4x - 3y = 33$
   $3x + 5y = 3$

11 $9x + 4y = -21$
   $5x - 7y = 16$

12 $10x + 9y = -14$
   $3x + 7y = 13$

13 $6x - y = 3$
   $3x + 5y = -4$

14 $8x + 6y = -1$
   $2x - 5y = 3$

15 $4x + 3y = 2$
   $2x + y = -1$

HWK 4M   **Main Book Page 202**

Form simultaneous equations then find the two unknown numbers in each question.

1 The sum of two numbers is 12. Twice one number subtract the other number is 9.
(eg. let the two numbers be x and y)

2 The difference between two numbers is 7. Double one number added to double the other number makes 62.

3 Treble one number added to the other number makes 71. The sum of the numbers is 29.

4 The difference between four times the larger number and the smaller number is 25. Double the larger number is equal to five less than treble the smaller number.

5 A school shop sells folders at £3 each and pens at £4 each. One day the shop sells 19 of these items and receives £70. How many folders were sold and how many pens were sold?

6

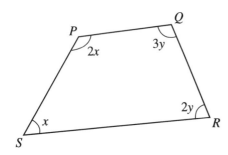

Angle P is 64° greater than angle R. Write down the value of each angle in this quadrilateral.

7

x	x	y	x	70
y	x	y	x	76
y	z	x	z	76
60	51	60	51	

In this rectangle the sum of the numbers in each row and each column is given. Find the values of x, y and z. (Hint: Find x and y first)

1 289 people turn up to play at a competition day involving football teams and rugby teams. Each football team has 11 players and each rugby team has 15 players. There are 23 teams in total. How many football teams are there and how many rugby teams are there? (Let the number of football teams be x and let the number of rugby teams be y)

2 One day a shop sells 103 copies of either a detective book or a science fiction book. These sales bring in £888. The detective book costs £9 and the science fiction book costs £8. How many of each type of book did the shop sell on that day?

3

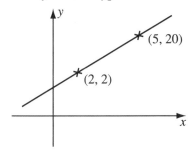

The line $y = mx + c$ passes through the points shown. Use simultaneous equations to find the values of m and c.

4 Each day in a local factory a machinist works for 6 hours and a packer works for 10 hours. 37 machinists and packers worked last Tuesday for a combined total of 274 hours. Exactly how many machinists and how many packers worked last Tuesday?

5 Angle x is 9° greater than angle y. Find the values of x and y.

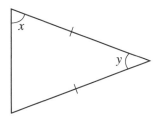

6 The curve with equation $y = ax^2 + k$ passes through the points (1, 8) and (3, 48). Find the values of a and k.

7 In a theatre, tickets in the stalls cost £20 each and other tickets cost £14 each. One night 512 people attend the theatre and pay a total of £8380 for their tickets. How many people sit in the stalls?

8 Here are three simultaneous equations. Find x, y and z.

$x + y + z = 11$

$x + 2y + z = 14$

$4x - 2y + 2z = 14$

9 Find a, b and c for the simultaneous equations below:

$3a + b + c = 16$

$a + 2b - 2c = 15$

$7a + b + c = 36$

UNIT 5

5.1 Trigonometry

In questions **1** to **8** use sine to find the required length, correct to 3 significant figures.

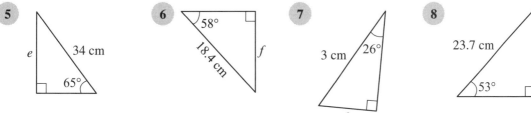

1 8 cm, a, 29°

2 b, 35°, 6.4 cm

3 43°, 5.9 cm, c

4 41°, 11 cm, d

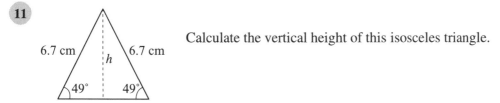

5 e, 34 cm, 65°

6 58°, 18.4 cm, f

7 3 cm, 26°, g

8 23.7 cm, h, 53°

9 A bird is 62 m away from a person on the ground at an angle of 38° to the ground. How high is the bird above the ground?

10 B is north of A. A boat is 18 km from A and due east of B. How far east of B is the boat if it is on a bearing of 057° from A?

11

6.7 cm, h, 6.7 cm, 49°, 49°

Calculate the vertical height of this isosceles triangle.

12 A 32 inch TV screen is shown opposite. Find the value of h.

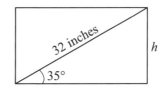

32 inches, h, 35°

In questions ① to ⑧ find the sides marked with letters, correct to 3 significant figures.
All lengths are in cm.

①

a
$32°$ 9 cm

②
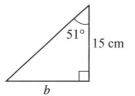
$51°$ 15 cm
b

③
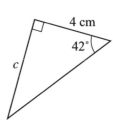
4 cm
$42°$
c

④
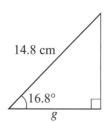
23 cm
d
$64°$

⑤
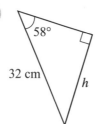
e
$53.4°$
9.6 cm

⑥
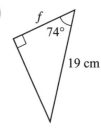
f
$74°$
19 cm

⑦
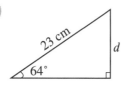
14.8 cm
$16.8°$
g

⑧
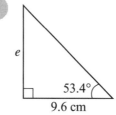
$58°$
32 cm
h

⑨ In triangle PQR, $\hat{PQR} = 90°$, $\hat{RPQ} = 48°$, RP = 12 cm. Find PQ.

⑩ In triangle ABC, $\hat{ACB} = 90°$, $\hat{ABC} = 62°$, BC = 17 cm. Find AC.

⑪ In triangle MNP, $\hat{PMN} = 90°$, $\hat{MNP} = 57°$, NP = 45 cm. Find MN.

⑫ Calculate the value of each letter, correct to 3 s.f.

(a)

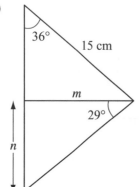
$36°$ 15 cm
m
$29°$
n

(b)
26 cm
x
$56°$
$32°$
y

89

HWK 3E ──────────────────────── Main Book Page 222

Give each answer to 3 significant figures when necessary.

1 The angle of elevation from a point P to the top of
a flagpole is 17°. Point P is 35 m from the base of
the flagpole. How tall is the flagpole?

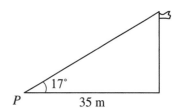

17°
P   35 m

2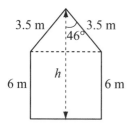

62°

A ladder of length 3.5 m rests against a vertical wall as shown.
How far up the wall does the ladder reach?

3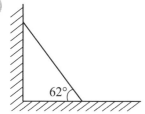

3.5 m   3.5 m
46°
h
6 m   6 m

Calculate the height of this house.

4 A ladder leans against a vertical wall so that the angle between
the ladder and the wall is 32°. The top of the ladder reaches 4.3 m up the wall.
How far from the wall is the base of the ladder?

5 A woman walks 7 km on a bearing of 075°. Calculate how far north
and how far east she is now from her starting point.

6 Calculate the area of the triangle shown opposite.

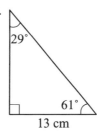

29°

61°
13 cm

7

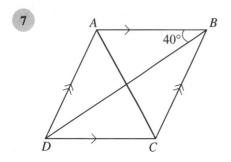

The diagonals AC and BD of a rhombus cross at right angles and bisect each other. Calculate the lengths of the diagonals if each side of the rhombus is 6 cm.

HWK 4M ──────────────────────────── **Main Book Page 223**

In questions **1** to **8** find the angles marked, correct to one decimal place. All lengths are in cm.

1

2
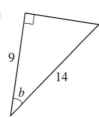

3
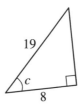

4
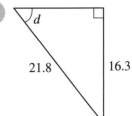

5
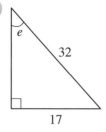

6
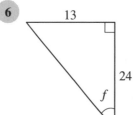

7
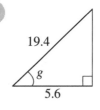

8
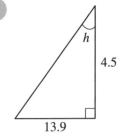

In questions **9** to **11** find the angles, correct to one decimal place.

9 In triangle MNP, MN̂P = 90°, MN = 16 cm, MP = 27 cm. Find PM̂N.

10 In triangle XYZ, XŶZ = 90°, XZ = 7.7 cm, YZ = 5.9 cm. Find YX̂Z.

11 In triangle ABC, AB̂C = 90°, BC = 23 cm, AC = 41 cm. Find AĈB.

Give each answer to one decimal place when necessary.

1 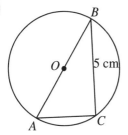 O is the centre of the circle. The radius of the circle is 4 cm.
AĈB = 90° because the angle in a semi-circle is a right angle.
Calculate the value of AB̂C.

2 Calculate the value of NP̂Q.

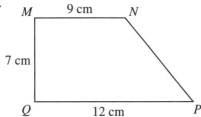

3 The base of a ladder is 1.8 m from a wall and the top of the ladder reaches 2.9 m up the wall. Calculate the angle between the ladder and the wall.

4 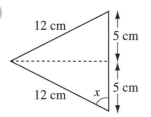 Calculate the value of *x* in this isosceles triangle.

5 A point P is 67 m away from the foot of a tree which is 7.4 m tall.
What is the angle of elevation to the top of the tree from point P?

6 A man walks 13 km due north then 6 km due east.
Find the bearing and distance of the man from his start position.

7 Calculate angle *x*, the angle in the roof of this house.

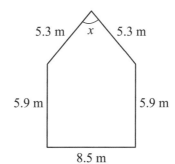

8

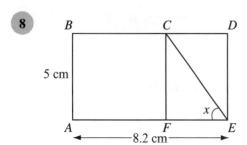

ABCF is a square. Calculate the value of angle *x*.

9

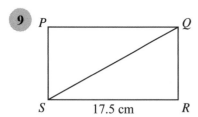

Calculate SQ̂R if the area of this rectangle is 136.5 cm².

10 The area of a parallelogram is given by:
base *b* × perpendicular height *h*

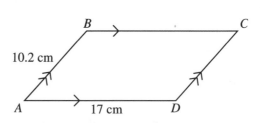

Calculate BÂD if the area of this
parallelogram is 141.1 cm².

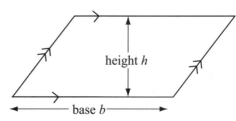

HWK 5M ———————————————— **Main Book Page 226**

Give the answers to 3 significant figures when required. Find the hypotenuse in each triangle.

1

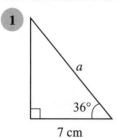

2

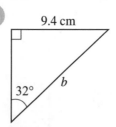

3

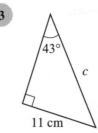

4 5.8 cm 57°
d

5 16 cm 62°
e

6 12.3 cm
f
74°

7 18.6 cm 49°
g

8 h
51°
25 cm

| **HWK 5E** | **Main Book Page 227** |

Give the answers to 3 significant figures when required.

1 Find the lengths *x* and *y* of each of
the sloping parts of the roof opposite.

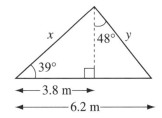

x   48°   y
39°
←3.8 m→
←6.2 m→

2 A balloon wants to fly from A to B which are 5 km apart.
A strong wind blows the balloon off course by an
angle of 41° as shown opposite. How far has
the balloon travelled when it reaches point C?

A   5 km   B
41°
C

3
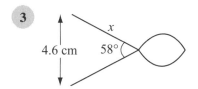
x
4.6 cm   58°

This logo design is to be drawn accurately. Calculate *x* to
find out how long each straight line must be drawn.

4 A ship sails due north for 15 km then due west to a point P. Point P is on a bearing of 314°
from the start position. How far is point P from the start position?

5 A ladder leans at an angle of 62° to the ground. The foot of the ladder is 2.2 m from
the wall. How long is the ladder?

6

Calculate the length *x*.

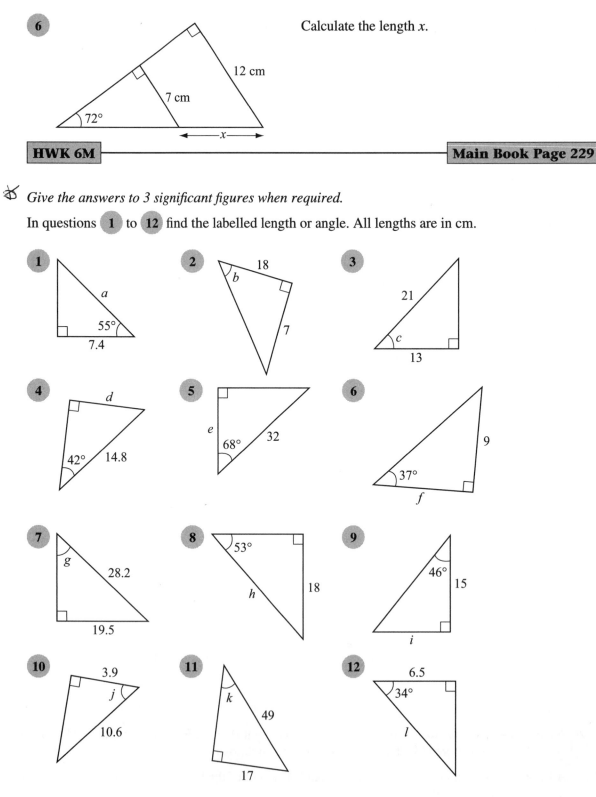

12 cm

7 cm

72°

x

HWK 6M ———————————————————————— **Main Book Page 229**

Give the answers to 3 significant figures when required.

In questions **1** to **12** find the labelled length or angle. All lengths are in cm.

1

a

55°

7.4

2

18

b

7

3

21

c

13

4

d

42°   14.8

5

e

68°   32

6

9

37°

f

7

g

28.2

19.5

8

53°

h

18

9

46°   15

i

10

3.9

j

10.6

11

k

49

17

12

6.5

34°

l

13 Calculate the lengths:

(a) BD

(b) CD

(c) AC

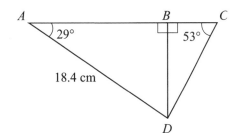

HWK 6E ———————————————————— **Main Book Page 230**

Give the answers to 3 significant figures when required.

1 Find x in each diagram. All lengths are in cm.

(a)

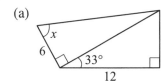

(b)

(c)

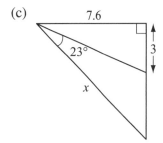

2

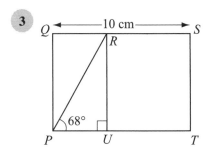

The two extreme positions of a car windscreen wiper are shown opposite. If the shortest distance between the ends of the wiper in the two positions is 64 cm, calculate the length of the windscreen wiper.

3

The area of rectangle PQST is 82.5 cm². Calculate the area of triangle PRU.

4 Calculate the area of a regular hexagon with each side equal to 5 cm.

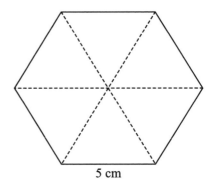

5 cm

5 Joe walks from his camp for 6 km on a bearing of 128° then walks on a bearing of 046° until he is due east of his camp. He now walks directly back to camp. How far has he walked in total?

6 The diagram opposite shows part of the steel framework for a new building. Each line represents a steel girder. The curved section is part of the circumference of a circle with its centre at the point P. Calculate the total length of steel used.

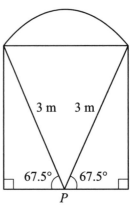

5.2 Inequalities

HWK 1M ———————————————————————— **Main Book Page 233**

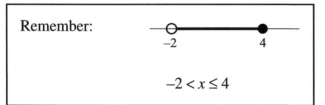

Remember:

$-2 < x \leq 4$

1 Answer true or false:

(a) $5 > -6$ (b) $-2 > -5$ (c) $4.2 > 4.16$

(d) $4^2 < 3^3$ (e) $30 \text{ mm} < 4 \text{ cm}$ (f) $2.3 \text{ kg} > 2245 \text{ g}$

2 Write down the inequalities displayed. Use x for the variable.

(a)
5

(b)
2

(c)
−3

(d)
4

(e)
−3   1

(f)
0   7

(g)
−6   −1

(h)
5

(i)
−8   3

3 Draw a number line like those in question **2** to display the following inequalities.

(a) $x \geq 3$

(b) $x < -4$

(c) $x \geq -1$

(d) $-4 \leq x \leq 2$

(e) $3 < x < 9$

(f) $-1 < x \leq 6$

(g) $x > 0$

(h) $4 \leq x < 10$

(i) $-7 < x \leq -2$

4 Write a possible number to complete each of the following:

(a) $\square > 1635$

(b) $-4 \leq \square < -3.9$

(c) $-8 > \square$

5 Carl's weight w is 76.12 kg. Tanya says that $w \geq 76.12$. Is Tanya correct?

6 Write an inequality for each statement.

(a) The minimum percentage, p, for a pass in a maths exam is 45%.

(b) The maximum number of pupils, n, in a class is 31.

(c) A restaurant must average between 15 and 20 customers, c, each evening in order to make enough money.

(d) The greatest height, h, for a child to play on a bouncy castle is 158 cm.

7 The variable x satisfies each of these inequalities:

$1 < x < 4$ and $2 \leq x \leq 8$

Mark the solution set for x on a number line.

HWK 2M ———————————————————— **Main Book Page 235**

Reminder: an integer is a positive or negative whole number or 0.
eg….., −3, −2, −1, 0, 1, 2, 3, …..

1 Write down all the integer values of n which satisfy the inequalities given below:

(a) $2 \leq n < 6$

(b) $-3 < n < 1$

(c) $0 \leq n \leq 5$

(d) $-5 < n \leq 4$

(e) $0 < 3n < 12$

(f) $-6 < 2n \leq 0$

2 Write down the smallest integer n such that

$4n > 39$

3 Solve the inequalities below:

(a) $x + 4 < 12$ (b) $3x - 1 \geq 17$ (c) $5x > 80$

(d) $x - 7 \leq -3$ (e) $10 + x < 13$ (f) $x - 4 \geq -6$

(g) $7x > 56$ (h) $3y \leq 1$ (i) $2x - 1 < 23$

4 Find the range of values of x which satisfy each of the following inequalities and show the answer on a number line.

(a) $6 + x < 11$ (b) $\frac{x}{4} \geq 5$ (c) $\frac{x}{2} \leq 4$

(d) $3x - 2 \leq 10$ (e) $9 + x > 1$ (f) $6x < -30$

In questions **5** to **8** list the solutions which satisfy the given conditions.

5 $1 < n < 10$; n is an odd number

6 $\frac{5x}{3} < 10$; x is a positive integer

7 $\frac{p}{4} < 3$; p is a prime number

8 $5n - 2 \geq 7n - 8$; n is a positive integer

9 State the smallest integer for which $3x > 11$

10 State the largest integer for which $7x - 3 < 34$

HWK 2E   **Main Book Page 236**

1 Solve the inequalities below:

(a) $\frac{3x + 1}{4} \geq 7$ (b) $2 - 5x < 7$ (c) $4 \leq 3(1 - 2x)$

(d) $4(2x + 3) < 3(x - 2)$ (e) $\frac{3 - 2x}{-4} \geq 1$ (f) $-6x < \frac{3(1 - 2x)}{5}$

2 Solve each pair of inequalities and then find the range of values of x for which both inequalities are true.

(a) $3x + 2 < 0$ and $2x + 3 > -1$ (b) $6 - x < 4$ and $\frac{x}{3} - 2 < 1$

(c) $4x + 3 < 8$ and $\frac{x}{2} + 1 > 0$ (d) $2(2x - 1) > 1$ and $12 - 3x > 5$

3 If $4^x > 5000$, what is the smallest whole number value of x.

4 If $2x + 1 < 7$ and $1 - 4x < 14$, list all the possible integer values of x.

5 Given that $2 \leq x \leq 8$ and $1 \leq y \leq 10$, find

    (a) the least possible value of $x - y$

    (b) the greatest possible value of $\dfrac{x}{y}$

    (c) the greatest possible value of $x^2 - y^2$

6 Find the smallest whole number n such that

$$\frac{138}{n+6} < \frac{1}{0.08}$$

7 Solve $2\left(\dfrac{1}{3}\right)^x \leq \dfrac{1}{2}$ giving your answer to 2 decimal places.

HWK 3E ——————————————————————————— **Main Book Page 237**

1 Write down three inequalities to describe fully each shaded region.

(a)

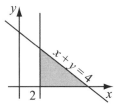

(b)

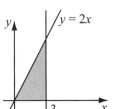

(c)

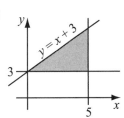

(d)

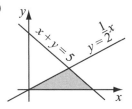

(e)

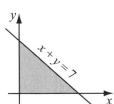

(f)

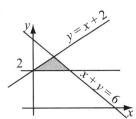

2 Draw sketch graphs and shade the regions indicated.

    (a) $y \leq x,\ y \geq 0,\ x + y \leq 3$ (b) $y \leq 6,\ y \geq x,\ x + y \geq 6$

    (c) $y \leq 4,\ x \leq 4,\ x + y \geq 4$ (d) $y \leq 2,\ y \leq 3x,\ y \geq \dfrac{1}{2}x$

5.3 Probability

1 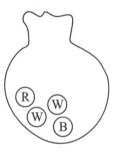 One card is picked at random from the cards shown opposite.
Find the probability that it is
(a) a '√'
(b) not a 'O'
(c) a '×' or a 'O'

2 A fair dice is rolled 270 times. How many times would you expect to roll a five?

3 | 5 | | 7 | | 7 | | 9 | | 9 | | 9 | | 11 |

One card is picked at random from the cards shown above.
Find the probability that it is
(a) a multiple of 3
(b) more than 7
(c) a prime number

4

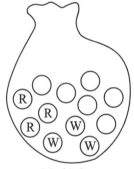

Gemma's bag

Mark's bag

Gemma and Mark each have a bag of balls which are red, white or blue.

(a) How many more of Mark's balls are white if he has the same probability of drawing out a white ball as Gemma?

(b) How many of Mark's balls might be blue if he has less chance of drawing out a blue ball than Gemma?

5

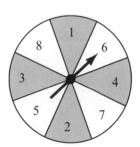

This spinner is spun 360 times.

How often would you expect to get:

(a) an odd number?

(b) a multiple of 3?

(c) a square number?

6 The probability of Amy being late to school on any day is 0.4.
How many times would you expect Amy to be on time for school during
a term of 60 days?

7 A bag contains red, yellow and green balls
as shown opposite.

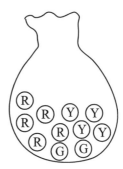

(a) Find the probability of selecting
a yellow ball?

(b) Six more red balls are added to the bag.
Find the probability of selecting a green ball.

HWK 2E ——————————————————————— **Main Book Page 243**

1 A shoe is thrown into the air. The probability of it landing 'heel down' is 63%.

(a) What is the probability of it not landing 'heel down'?

(b) How many times would you expect the shoe to land 'heel down' if it is
thrown 400 times?

2 The probability of throwing a double six with two dice is $\frac{1}{36}$.
What is the probability of *not* throwing a double six?

3

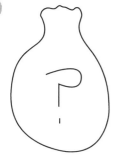

A bag contains red and blue balls. The probability of picking
a blue ball is $\frac{5}{9}$.

There are more than 10 balls in this bag.

Write down how many red balls could be in this bag?

4

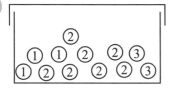

One number is selected at random from
the box and then replaced.

This is done 600 times. How many times
would you expect to select:

(a) the number '1'?

(b) the number '2'?

5 A box contains 100 beads. There are *n* green beads and the remaining beads are yellow. Write
down an expression for the probability of selecting a yellow bead.

6 Martin has a bag with 6 blue balls and 1 green ball. He says the probability of taking out a green ball is $\frac{1}{6}$.

Is he correct? Give a reason for your answer.

7 A box contains x red balls, y blue balls and 5 yellow balls. One ball is selected from the box. What is the probability of selecting a red or blue ball?

8 When Carl plays darts, he has a 0.5% chance of hitting the bullseye with his next dart. During an evening he will throw on average 250 darts. He plays on 3 evenings a week. How many times would you expect Carl to hit the bullseye over a 4 week period?

9 There are 16 red beads, n green beads and 24 yellow beads in a bag. One bead is removed at random. Given that the probability that it is green is $\frac{1}{11}$, calculate the value of n.

HWK 3M/3E ──────────────────────────────── **Main Book Page 245**

1 A bag contains a £5 note, a £10 note and a £20 note. Two notes are selected at random.

(a) List all the possible combinations of two notes which can be selected from the bag.

(b) Find the probability that the total value of the two notes selected is

    (i) £30   (ii) £25   (iii) £15

2 Emma spins the spinner and throws the dice. She might get a 'B' and a '4', ie. B4.

(a) List all the possible outcomes.

(b) What is the probability of getting a 'C' with an even number?

3 (a) A set of triplets is born. List all the possible boy/girl outcomes for the three babies. Assume that there is an even chance of having a boy or a girl.

(b) What is the probability of having 3 girls?

(c) What is the probability of having 2 boys and a girl?

4 Four children take the bus to school each morning. Ben always pushes his way onto the bus first. Helen, Ramsay and Louise then get onto the bus in any order.

(a) Write down the possible orders of the four children getting onto the bus.

(b) What is the probability of Louise being the second person to get onto the bus?

5

Den has two spinners. He spins both spinners and adds up the numbers to get a total.

(a) Make a list of all the possible totals.

(b) What is the probability of getting a total of 9?

6 What is the probability of getting 3 sixes when 3 dice are rolled?

7 (a) List all the ways of arranging the 3 letters $\boxed{A}$, $\boxed{B}$ and $\boxed{C}$. For example, CAB. How many different ways did you find?

(b) List all the ways of arranging the 4 letters $\boxed{A}$, $\boxed{B}$, $\boxed{C}$ and $\boxed{D}$. How many different ways did you find?

(c) Look for a pattern. How many different ways can 5 letters be arranged?

(d) How many different ways can 10 letters be arranged?

HWK 4M/4E ──────────────────────────── **Main Book Page 247**

---

1 The probability of Kate having a cup of tea in the morning is $\frac{9}{10}$. What is the probability of Kate not having a cup of tea in the morning?

2 Jake has only £20, £10 and £5 notes in his wallet. The next time he buys something, he uses one of these notes. The probability of using a £5 note is 0.1. The probability of using a £10 note is 0.5. What is the probability that he uses a £20 note?

3 Wayne, Janice, Helen and Dom play a game of cards. The probability of each person winning is shown in the table below.

Name	Wayne	Janice	Helen	Dom
Probability of winning	0.3	0.15	x	0.2

Find the probability of

(a) Janice or Dom winning

(b) Helen winning

(c) Janice *not* winning

(d) How many times would you expect Wayne to win if they play 20 games?

4 A bag contains red, green, blue and yellow balls. The table shows the probability of each colour being drawn when one ball is removed from the bag.

red	0.35
green	n
blue	0.18
yellow	0.24

What is the probability of drawing

(a) a green ball?

(b) a blue or yellow ball?

(c) *not* a blue ball?

5 The probability of Hatton United winning their next football game is $\frac{2}{3}$.

The probability of Hatton United losing their next football game is $\frac{1}{4}$.

What is the probability of Hatton United drawing their next football game?

6 Sadie either walks, cycles or gets driven to school each morning.

The probability of walking is 0.38

Sadie is twice as likely to walk as to cycle. What is the probability that Sadie will get driven to school?

7 The table below shows the probabilities of different types of animal being the next to arrive at an Animal Rescue Centre.

animal	cat	dog	rabbit	guinea pig	other
probability	$\frac{3}{10}$	$\frac{2}{5}$	x	$\frac{1}{10}$	$\frac{1}{20}$

Find the probability of the next animal being

(a) a cat or a dog

(b) a rabbit

(c) Out of the next 80 animals brought to the Animal Rescue Centre, how many would you expect to be dogs?

5.4 Gradient of a line, $y = mx + c$

HWK 1M — **Main Book Page 250**

> Remember: $\quad$ gradient of a line $= \dfrac{\text{difference between } y \text{ coordinates}}{\text{difference between } x \text{ coordinates}}$

1 Find the gradient of:

(a) line AB

(b) line CD

(c) line EF

(d) line GH

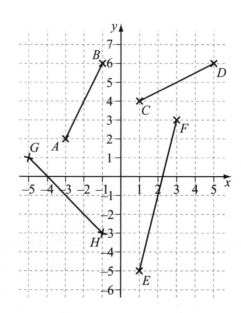

2 Find the gradient of the line joining

   (a) (4, 2) and (6, 10)   (b) (2, 1) and (5, 22)   (c) (1, 3) and (3, 5)

   (d) (2, 4) and (6, 16)   (e) (2, 5) and (4, 6)   (f) (1, –4) and (–2, 2)

   (g) (–3, –5) and (1, –1)   (h) (4, –3) and (–1, 27)

3 Answer true or false:

   'The line joining (–3, 2) and (2, 17) is parallel to the line joining (4, –6) and (6, 0)'.

4 Find the gradient of the line joining:

   (a) P and Q

   (b) Q and R

   (c) P and R

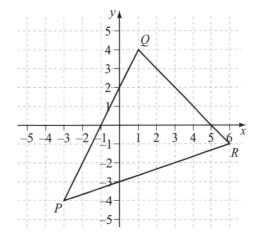

HWK 2M	**Main Book Page 250**

1 Give the gradient and *y*-intercept of each line.

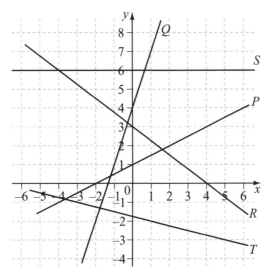

2 *Sketch* the following straight lines. Use a new pair of axes for each question.

(a) Gradient 1, y-intercept 2

(b) Gradient 3, y-intercept –4

(c) Gradient –2, y-intercept 3

(d) Gradient 2, y-intercept –5

(e) Gradient $\frac{1}{2}$, y-intercept –1

(f) Gradient $-\frac{1}{3}$, y-intercept 0

HWK 3M —————————————————————————— **Main Book Page 251**

Write down the gradient and y-intercept of each of the following lines:

1 $y = 4x - 1$

2 $y = 2x + 9$

3 $y = -4x + 3$

4 $y = \frac{1}{3}x + 6$

5 $y = \frac{1}{4}x - 3$

6 $y = -x - 2$

7 $y = 3 - 2x$

8 $y = 6 + 4x$

9 $y = 4 - \frac{1}{3}x$

In questions **10** to **18** make y the subject and write down the gradient and intercept of the corresponding line.

10 $3x + y - 5 = 0$

11 $4x + y + 3 = 0$

12 $y - x + 4 = 0$

13 $5x - y + 2 = 0$

14 $5x + 7y + 1 = 0$

15 $3x - 4y + 2 = 0$

16 $2y + 5x - 1 = 0$

17 $2x - 3y - 7 = 0$

18 $9y + 2x + 4 = 0$

HWK 3E —————————————————————————— **Main Book Page 252**

1 Use the gradient and intercept to write down the equation of the lines P, Q and R.

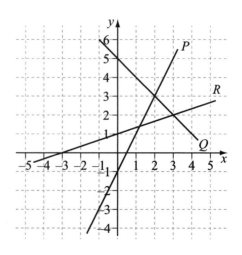

2 Write down which of the two lines below meet at the same point on the *y*-axis.

$y = 4x + 3$ $y = 3x + 4$ $y = 3 - 2x$

In questions **3** to **8** match each sketch with the correct equation from the list below.

3
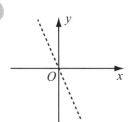

4
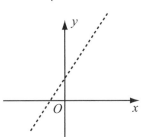

5
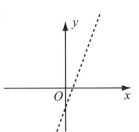

6
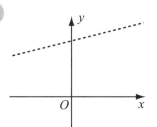

7
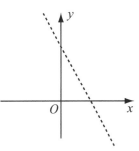

8
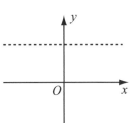

    (a) $y = 3x + 1$ (b) $y = -2x$ (c) $y = \frac{1}{2}x + 5$

    (d) $y = 4 - 2x$ (e) $y = 3$ (f) $y = 4x - 2$

9 Sketch each of the following lines:

    (a) $y = 2x - 2$ (b) $y = 5 - 3x$ (c) $y - x - 3 = 0$

    (d) $y + 2x - 6 = 0$ (e) $3x - y - 1 = 0$ (f) $4y - 8x + 1 = 0$

HWK 4E ──────────────────────────────────── **Main Book Page 253**

> Remember: For perpendicular lines the product of the gradients is –1

1 Write down the gradient of a line which is perpendicular to a line of gradient

    (a) 4   (b) –2   (c) $\frac{1}{3}$ (d) 1   (e) $-\frac{1}{5}$

2 Write down the equation of any line which is perpendicular to

    (a) $y = 3x + 4$ (b) $y = -\frac{1}{2}x + 3$ (c) $y = \frac{1}{4}x - 3$

3 Write down the equation of any line parallel to $y = x - 7$.

4 Find the equations of each of the lines below.

(a)
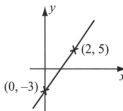

(b)
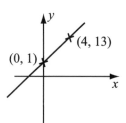

(c)
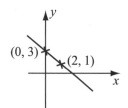

(d)
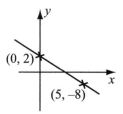

5 For each part of question **4** find the equation of the perpendicular line which meets the given line on the y-axis.

6 Write down the equation of any line parallel to $y = 2 - 6x$.

7 Two pairs of equations below represent lines which are perpendicular to each other. Write down the two pairs.

A $\boxed{y = 2x + 4}$ B $\boxed{y = 1 - 5x}$ C $\boxed{y = 3 - 2x}$ D $\boxed{y = \frac{1}{5}x - 4}$

E $\boxed{y = -\frac{1}{3}x + 1}$ F $\boxed{y = -\frac{1}{5}x + 3}$ G $\boxed{y = \frac{1}{2}x + 2}$ H $\boxed{y = -\frac{1}{4}x + 5}$

8 Find the equation of the line which is perpendicular to $y = 0.2x - 3$ and passes through $(0, 7)$.

9   Find the equation of this line.

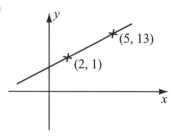

10 A line passes through $(0, -2)$ and is perpendicular to the line joining $(-3, -1)$ to $(2, 14)$. Find the equation of this line.

5.5 Mathematical reasoning, proof

1 *Prove* that $\hat{Q}RS = x + y$

This is a proof for the exterior angle of
a triangle being equal to the sum of
the two opposite interior angles.

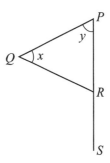

2 *Prove* that the difference between 2 odd numbers is even.
(Hint: let one odd number $= 2n + 1$ and the other odd number $= 2m + 1$)

3 *Prove* that the sum of 3 consecutive whole numbers is always divisible by 3.

4 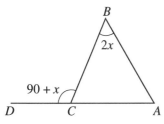 *Prove* that triangle ABC is isosceles.

5 *Prove* that $a + b = 270°$ in the diagram opposite.

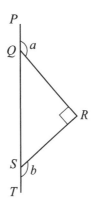

6 *Prove* that the difference between the squares of 2 consecutive whole numbers is odd.

7

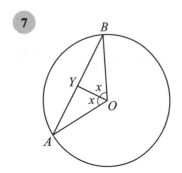

O is the centre of the circle.

The line OY bisects AÔB as shown.

Use congruent triangles to *prove* that OY bisects AB (ie. cuts AB in half)

UNIT 6

6.1 Drawing and using graphs

HWK 1M ——————————————————————————— **Main Book Page 271**

1 (a) Copy and complete the table for $y = 2x - 4$

x	−2	−1	0	1	2	3
2x	−4	−2				
−4	−4	−4		−4		
y	−8	−6				

(b) Draw the graph using the axes shown.

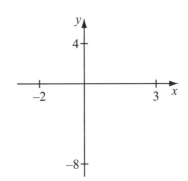

2 Draw $y = 3x - 1$ for x-values from −3 to 3.

3 (a) Draw an x-axis from 0 to 5 and a y-axis from 0 to 16.

(b) On the same graph, draw the lines $y = 2x + 6$ and $y = 12 - x$

(c) Write down the co-ordinates of the point where the two lines intersect each other.

4 (a) Draw an x-axis from −2 to 8 and a y-axis from −2 to 11.

(b) Draw the lines $y = 2x + 2$, $x = 4$, $y = 8 - x$ and $y = 2$.

(c) Work out the difference between the area enclosed by the lines $y = 2x + 2$, $y = 8 - x$, $y = 2$ and the area enclosed by the lines $y = 2x + 2$, $x = 4$, $y = 8 - x$.

HWK 2M ——————————————————————————— **Main Book Page 272**

1 (a) Copy and complete the table for $y = x^2 + 1$

x	−3	−2	−1	0	1	2	3
x^2	9	4					
+1	1	1	1				
y	10						

(b) Draw the graph using the axes shown.

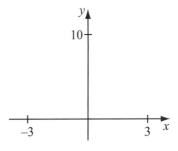

112

2 (a) Copy and complete the table for $y = x^2 + 3x$

x	–5	–4	–3	–2	–1	0	1	2
x^2	25							4
$3x$	–15	–12						6
y	10							10

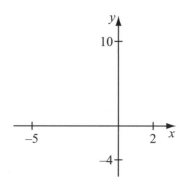

(b) Draw the graph using the axes shown.

(c) What is the equation of the line of symmetry?

3 (a) Draw the graph of $y = x^2 + 4x - 3$ for x-values from –5 to 1.

(b) Write down the co-ordinates of the lowest point on the curve.

4 (a) Draw the graph of $y = x^2 - 6x + 4$ from –1 to 5.

(b) What is the equation of the line of symmetry?

HWK 2E ———————————————————————— **Main Book Page 273**

1 Draw $y = 3x^2 - x$ for x-values from –3 to 3.

2 Draw $y = x^3 - x$ for x-values from –3 to 3.

3 Draw $y = \dfrac{10}{x}$ for x-values from 1 to 10.

4 (a) Draw $y = x^2 - 3x - 1$ for x-values from –2 to 4.

(b) On the same axes draw $y = 2 - x$.

(c) Write down the co-ordinates of the points of intersection.

5 (a) Copy and complete this table for $y = 3^x$.

x	–3	–2	–1	0	1	2	3
y	0.04	0.1					

(b) Draw the graph for $y = 3^x$

(c) On the same axes draw $y = \frac{1}{2}x + 3$

(d) Use your graph to solve $3^x = \frac{1}{2}x + 3$

(i.e. find the x-values where the line $y = \frac{1}{2}x + 3$ meets the curve $y = 3^x$)

6.2 Compound measures

HWK 1M **Main Book Page 275**

Remember: speed = $\dfrac{\text{distance}}{\text{time}}$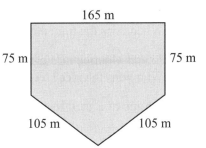

1 A car travels a distance of 300 m at a speed of 15 m/s. How long does it take?

2 A ship sails 168 km in 14 hours. How fast does it travel?

3 A man walks 0.8 km in 10 minutes. What is his speed in kilometres per hour?

4 A dog runs at a speed of 11.5 m/s. How far will the dog run in 6 seconds?

5 A coach travels at a speed of 76 km/h. How far does it travel in 2 hours 30 minutes?

6 A woman jogs around the edge of the park shown opposite. How long will it take her to jog around the edge of the park four times, if her average speed is 3 m/s? Give your answer in minutes and seconds.

165 m
75 m   75 m
105 m   105 m

7 A car travels 14 miles in 12 minutes. What is its speed in miles per hour?

8 A train travels at an average speed of 94 miles per hour. How far will it travel in 1 hour 15 minutes?

9 It takes 20 minutes for Stuart to cycle 7.2 km. How far does he travel in 2 hours?

10 Jack walks 28.8 km in 6 hours. Cheryl walks 1.24 km every 15 minutes. Who walks further in one hour and by how much?

HWK 1E **Main Book Page 276**

1 Find the time taken for the following:

(a)	2.5 miles at 10 mph
(b)	3 km at 50 m/s (note the units)
(c)	612 km at 18 km/h
(d)	2000 m at 8 km/h

114

2 A vehicle travels for 16s at a speed of 17 m/s. How far does it travel?

3 A sprinter covers 7m in 0.8s. Find the sprinter's speed.

4 Penny walks at a speed of 6 km/h for 40 minutes. Darryl travels the same distance at a steady speed of 5 km/h. How long does Darryl walk for?

5 An astronomer is recording the path of a comet. The comet changes position by 92 km in 3 minutes. What is the speed of the comet in km/h?

6 Find the distance travelled using the information opposite.

(a)	3 cm/hour for 2 days
(b)	13 mph for 9 hours
(c)	20 m/s for 3 hours
(d)	4.5 m/s for 5 minutes

7 A ship sails at a speed of 12 knots for one day. How far does it travel?
(1 knot = 1 nautical mile per hour)

8 A train travels 315 km from London to York at an average speed of 175 km/h. When does the train arrive in York if it leaves London at 1315?

9 Jo and Maurice race against each other. Jo runs at 6 m/s and Maurice runs at 21 km/h. Who wins the race? You *must* show all your working out.

10 Jerome runs at a steady speed of 12 km/h for 3 hours 12 minutes. How far does Jerome run?

11 An athlete completes $8\frac{1}{2}$ laps on the running track shown opposite. The athlete runs at a steady speed and takes 9 minutes 24 seconds. Calculate the athlete's speed in km/h.

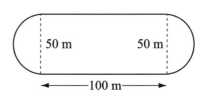

50 m   50 m
—100 m—

HWK 2M   **Main Book Page 277**

Remember: Density = $\frac{\text{Mass}}{\text{Volume}}$ Mass = Density × Volume

1 The mass of 45 cm³ of copper is 405 grams. What is the density of the copper?

2 The density of lead is 11.4 g/cm³. Calculate the weight of 300 cm³ of lead.

3 Find the volume of a piece of zinc which weighs 1308 g. The density of zinc is 6 g/cm³.

4 Copy and complete the table:

Density (g/cm³)	Mass (g)	Volume (cm³)
12		15
	56	7
8	192	
	3	0.5
5.6		20

5 The density of silk is 1.3 g/cm³. What is the mass of 9 cm³ of silk?

6 Which weighs more; 35 cm³ of iron with density 7.5 g/cm³ or 13 cm³ of gold with density 19 g/cm³?

7 If £1 = 1.15 euros,

(a) change £750 into euros.

(b) change 69 euros into pounds.

(c) Anna buys a dress for 57.50 euros when on holiday in Spain. When she gets back to London, she finds the same dress on sale for £52. Which was the better deal – Spain or London? *Explain* why you make your choice.

8

£1 = $1.45 (USA)
£1 = 185 yen (Japan)

(a) Change 6475 yen into pounds.

(b) Change £180 into dollars.

(c) Marie brings 13320 yen back from her holiday in Japan.
Cornelius brings $98.60 back from his stay in New York.
Who brings the most money back? *Explain* why you make your choice.

HWK 2E ———————————————————— **Main Book Page 278**

1 Some dress material costs £34 per metre. How much will 1.6 m cost?

2 26 m² of carpet costs £598. What is the cost per m² of the carpet?

3 Electrical cable costs £2.70 per metre.
What is the cost of laying this cable once completely
around the edge of this room?

2.9 m

4.6 m

4 It costs £19 per minute to run an industrial machine. The machine runs all day except for two stoppages each of two hours duration. How much does it cost to run the machine for one complete seven day week?

5 A rectangular metal bar has dimensions 6 cm × 4 cm × 3 cm.
Work out the weight of the metal bar if the metal density is 8 g/cm³.

6 A tile cutter is hired for 3 weeks. There is a fixed charge of £27 then a
cost of £6.50 per day. How much will the hire of the tile cutter cost in total?

7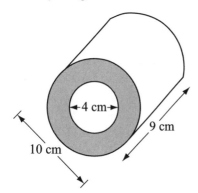
Raspberries are grown in this field. The farmer makes £2.25 per m².
How much money will the farmer make in total?

40 m

90 m

8 This metal cylinder has a cylindrical
hole drilled through it. The metal has
density 6.8 g/cm³.

This triangular prism is made
from metal with density 8.2 g/cm³.

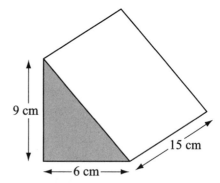

4 cm

9 cm

10 cm

9 cm

6 cm

15 cm

Which metal object weighs more and by how much? Give your answer to 3 significant figures.

9 A rock star earns 22p every second of the year. How much money does the rock star earn in
one year?

10 Eight coins are made from a metal with density 7.4 g/cm³.
Each coin has diameter 1.9 cm. The coins are stacked on
top of each other. How high is the stack of coins if their total
weight is 38.6 g? Give your answer to 3 significant figures.

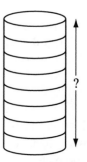

?

6.3 Locus

1

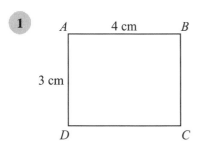

Draw this rectangle accurately. Shade an area inside the rectangle to show all the points which are less than or equal to 2 cm from the corner A.

2 Draw any two points P and Q. Draw the locus of all the points which are equidistant from P and Q. ('equidistant' means an equal distance, ie. the same length)

3

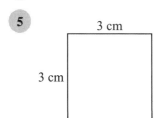

Draw three rectangles like this with a scale of 1 cm to 1 m. Use a different rectangle to draw each of the following loci:

(a) Points in the room equidistant from P and S.

(b) Points in the room which are more than or equal to 3 m from R.

(c) Points in the room which are equidistant from the lines PS and SR.

4 Draw a line AB of length 6 cm. Draw the locus of all the points which are 3 cm from the line AB.

5

3 cm

3 cm

Draw this square accurately.
Draw the locus of all the points which are exactly 1 cm from the edge of the square and outside the square.

6 Describe in words the locus of the tip of the hour hand on a clock as it moves from 6 o'clock to 12 o'clock.

7 One end of a piece of string attached to a ball is fixed to the top of a wooden post. The ball is hit horizontally and the string starts to wrap itself around the post. Sketch the locus of the path of the ball when viewed from above.

118

1 (a) Draw the places opposite
using a scale of 1cm to 5 km.

(b) Jacqui lives within 20 km of Benford
and within 15 km of Chowley.
On your diagram show the area
where Jacqui might live.

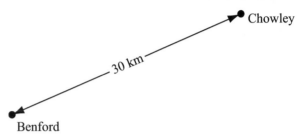

Chowley

30 km

Benford

2

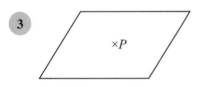

5 m

2 m

3 m

D

6 m

Draw a diagram of this yard using a scale of 1 cm to 1 m.
A dog is tied to the point D with a rope
2.5 m long.
Shade in the parts inside the yard which the dog
cannot reach.

3

×P

A point P is marked on the top of a table. Describe the
locus of points which are 5 cm from P either on
the table or above the table.

4 Draw this square. Show the locus of
points inside the square which are less than
4 cm from P and equidistant from PQ and PS.

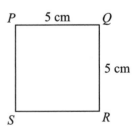

P 5 cm Q

5 cm

S R

5 Mark a point P on your paper. Shade the locus of points which are between 5 cm and 3 cm from P.

6 (a) Draw the diagram opposite using a
scale of 1 cm to 20 m

(b) A pipe is to be laid which is
equidistant from A and B
as well as being within 90 m of B.
Show clearly exactly where the pipe is to be laid.

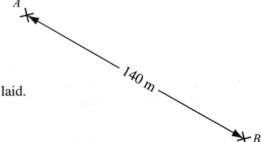

A

140 m

B

7 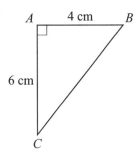 Draw this triangle. Show the locus of points which are nearer to BC than to AB.

8 Draw the diagram opposite.
All lengths are in cm.

Draw the locus of points which are at least 3 cm from A and nearer to D than to F.

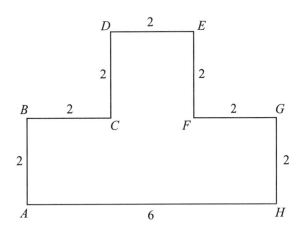

6.4 Changing the subject of a formula

HWK 1M —————————————————————— **Main Book Page 286**

In questions **1** to **12** make x the subject.

1 $x + v = m$ **2** $x - y = n$ **3** $x - b = a + c$ **4** $y + x = 4a + p$

5 $m + 2n = x - a$ **6** $x + ab = m$ **7** $bx = m$ **8** $x - mn = y$

9 $ax = m - n$ **10** $ax - b = c$ **11** $p = mx + y$ **12** $m = x - m^2$

In questions **13** to **24** make y the subject.

13 $2n = my - c$ **14** $by - n = 2n$ **15** $m + n = cy - p$ **16** $x^2 + ny = n^2$

17 $a + b = ny + c$ **18** $my = -n$ **19** $mny = a + b$ **20** $mny - p = a$

21 $a^2 + b^2y = c^2$ **22** $3ax + 5by = 2c$ **23** $5a^2 - b^2 = my + n^2$ **24** $p^3 = mny - p^3$

120

In questions **1** to **12** make x the subject.

1 $mn + yx = a^2$

2 $m(x + y) = n$

3 $x(a + b) = m$

4 $a(x - b) = y$

5 $3m = nx + m$

6 $(p - 2q)x = n$

7 $a^2 = m(x - n)$

8 $n^2(m + x) = y^2$

9 $mn(x - y) = a$

10 $b = yx(a + b)$

11 $m(a - b)x = n^2$

12 $p^2 - q^2 = m(x - p)$

13 Using the formula $a^2 = n(x + y) + b$

    (a) make x the subject   (b) make n the subject

14 Using the formula $(a - b)x = m^2 - n^2$

    (a) make x the subject   (b) make a the subject

Make x the subject.

1 $\dfrac{x}{a} = b$

2 $mn = \dfrac{x}{3}$

3 $m + n = \dfrac{x}{a}$

4 $\dfrac{x}{m + n} = y$

5 $\dfrac{m}{x} = n$

6 $\dfrac{x}{a} = 2m - n$

7 $p = \dfrac{x}{m}$

8 $m + n = \dfrac{a}{x}$

9 $\dfrac{a - b}{x} = p + q$

10 $3a + 2b = \dfrac{m}{x}$

11 $\dfrac{c - d}{x} = m - n$

12 $\dfrac{x}{m} = \dfrac{n}{y}$

13 $\dfrac{a}{c} = \dfrac{x}{n}$

14 $\dfrac{a}{x} = 3b - 2y$

15 $\dfrac{x}{2m + n} = 3b$

Make x the subject.

1 $\dfrac{m - n}{x} = y$

2 $a + b = \dfrac{m + 3d}{x}$

3 $\dfrac{a^2}{b} = \dfrac{x}{m + n}$

4 $\dfrac{ab}{x} = \dfrac{m^2}{n^2}$

5 $\dfrac{\pi x\,(a - b)}{y} = y$

6 $\dfrac{n}{x + a} = m$

7 $cd = \dfrac{m}{x - a}$

8 $\dfrac{a^2}{x} = b - y$

9 $\dfrac{m}{x + n} = \dfrac{a}{b}$

10 $\dfrac{m}{x} = \tan 30°$

11 $p = \dfrac{\pi}{x(a + b)}$

12 $\dfrac{a}{x + 2y} = 4\pi r^2$

13 $\dfrac{x + m}{\cos 43°} = n$

14 $\dfrac{a + b}{x \tan 36°} = \dfrac{m}{n}$

15 $\dfrac{2h - 3m}{x + 4n - a} = \dfrac{m}{p}$

────────────────

In questions **1** to **12** make x the subject.

1 $a - x = b$

2 $a^2 + b^2 = p - x$

3 $m^2 - x = n + y$

4 $p + 3q - x = 2n$

5 $p - mx = n$

6 $a^2 + m = b^2 - x$

7 $4m = n - bx$

8 $m^2 - ax = n^2$

9 $4n^2 - mx = 3p$

10 $mn = m + 2n - px$

11 $5a^2 - 4mx = b^2$

12 $p^2 - m^2 = a^2 - n^2x$

Remove the brackets in questions **13** to **21** and then make x the subject.

13 $a(n + x) = m$

14 $m(n - x) = y$

15 $n(p - x) = m^2$

16 $a(b - mx) = 3n$

17 $a^2 + y^2 = m(a - nx)$

18 $y(y^2 - ax) = m$

19 $mn(m - nx) = 4y$

20 $b^2 = a(m + n - x)$

21 $a^2(b^2 - ax) = n^2$

────────────────

In questions **1** to **12** make x the subject.

1 $\sqrt{x - m} = n$

2 $m\sqrt{x} = n$

3 $n\sqrt{x} = a - b$

4 $\sqrt{mx} = y$

5 $\sqrt{x} = \dfrac{m}{n}$

6 $4a = \sqrt{x + m}$

7 $\sqrt{\dfrac{x}{y}} = a$

8 $\sqrt{\dfrac{x}{mn}} = y$

9 $m = \sqrt{\dfrac{a}{x}}$

10 $\sqrt{\dfrac{3m}{x}} = p$

11 $\sqrt{\dfrac{n}{x}} = \dfrac{a}{y}$

12 $\sqrt{\dfrac{x - a}{4m}} = \dfrac{2n}{p}$

Now make n the subject of the formula.

13 $n^2 - y = m$

14 $a = n^2 + b$

15 $(n + y)^2 = x$

16 $b = (n - a)^2$

17 $pn^2 + m = a$

18 $\dfrac{mn^2}{p} = y$

19 $\dfrac{an^2}{y} - m = b$

20 $(pn + a)^2 = w$

21 $(a + 3mn)^2 = y$

22 $a - n^2 = p$

23 $3m = a + \dfrac{bn^2}{y}$

24 $\dfrac{(n - p)^2}{m} = 3a$

122

1 A well known scientific formula is $v^2 = u^2 + 2as$

where v = velocity, u = initial velocity, a = acceleration and s = displacement.

(a) Find v when $u = 6$, $a = 2$ and $s = 7$.

(b) Make u the subject of the formula.

(c) Find u when $v = 11$, $a = 9$ and $s = 4$.

2 The total surface area, A, of a cylinder is given by the formula

$A = 2\pi r (r + h)$

(a) Find A in terms of π when $r = 7$ and $h = 5$.

(b) Make h the subject of the formula.

(c) Find h when $r = 3$ and $A = 20\pi$.

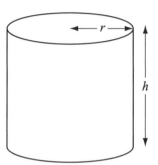

3 The volume, V, of a sphere is given by the formula $V = \frac{4}{3}\pi r^3$

(a) Make r the subject of the formula.

(b) Find r when $V = 288\pi$.

4

A particle suspended by a string of length l forms a simple pendulum. The particle swings as shown opposite. The time, T, which the particle takes to return to its starting position is given by the formula

$$T = 2\pi \sqrt{\frac{l}{g}}$$

where g is the acceleration due to gravity.

(a) Make l the subject of the formula.

(b) Find l when $g = 10$ and $T = \pi$.

5 The formula shown below is known as the cosine rule. It is used to work out missing lengths or angles in triangles.

$a^2 = b^2 + c^2 - 2bc \cos\hat{A}$

(a) Rearrange to make $\cos \hat{A}$ the subject of the formula.

(b) Find the value of $\hat{A}$ to the nearest degree when $a = 4$ cm, $b = 7$ cm and $c = 8$ cm.

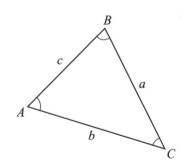

6.5 Similar shapes

HWK 1M ────────────────────────── **Main Book Page 291**

1 Which shapes
are similar to shape P?

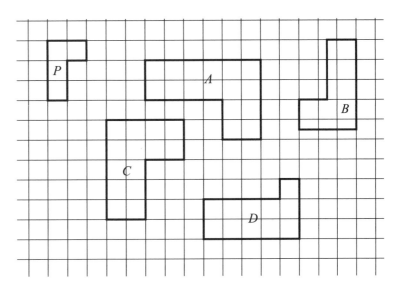

2 These pairs of shapes are similar. Find the lengths marked with letters. All lengths are in cm.

(a)
3.2, 5, 4.8, x

(b)
4, 6, 2, y, 15

(c)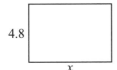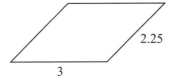
x, 2.4, 3, 2.25

(d)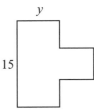
8, y, 9.6, 5.4

3 Is this statement true or false? 'Any two quarter circles are similar.'

4 These 3 rectangles are similar. Find the lengths *a* and *b*. All lengths are in cm.

 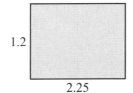 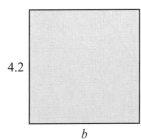
0.8, a, 1.2, 2.25, 4.2, b

124

5 Is this statement true or false? 'Any two kites are similar'.

6

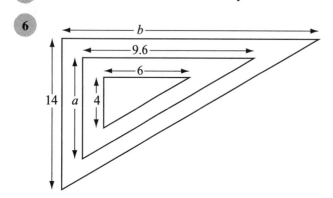

These 3 triangles are similar. All lengths are in cm. Find the lengths *a* and *b*.

HWK 2M ——————————————————————————— **Main Book Page 293**

1 Which pairs of triangles below are similar?

(a)
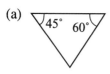

(b)

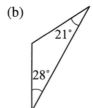

(c)
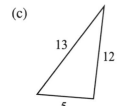
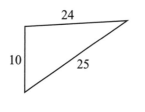

(d)
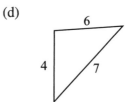
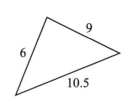

2 Find the sides marked with letters in these pairs of similar triangles. All lengths are in cm.

(a)
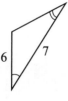
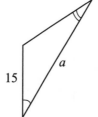

(b)

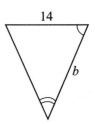

(c)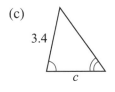

(d)

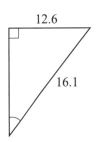

(e)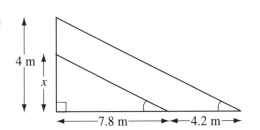

(f)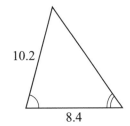

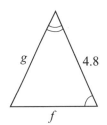

3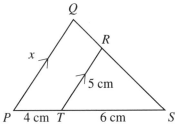

Find the value of x.

HWK 2E ———————————————————— **Main Book Page 295**

1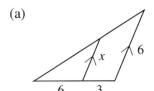

Triangles PQS and TRS are similar. Find the value of x.

2 Use similar triangles to find the lengths marked with letters. All lengths are in cm

(a)

(b)

(c)

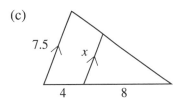

126

(d)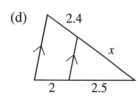
2.4
x
2   2.5

(e)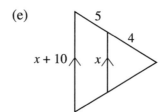
5
4
x + 10   x

(f)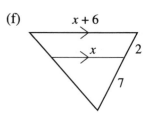
x + 6
x   2
7

3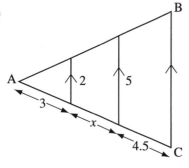

B
A
2   5
3
x
4.5   C

Use similar triangles to find the length BC.
All lengths are in cm.

4 Use similar triangles to find the lengths marked with letters. All lengths are in cm.

(a)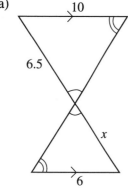
10
6.5
x
6

(b)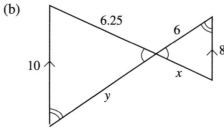
6.25
6
10   8
y   x

| HWK 3E | Main Book Page 296 |

1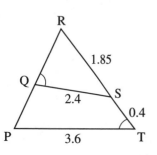

R
1.85
Q
2.4   S
0.4
P   3.6   T

$R\hat{Q}S = P\hat{T}R$
Find the length QR.
All the lengths are in cm.

2

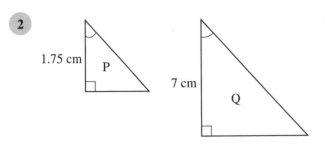

Triangles P and Q are similar.
The area of triangle Q is 31.5 cm².

(a) Find the area of triangle P.

(b) How many times larger is the area of triangle Q compared to the area of triangle P?
Is there a connection between this and the ratios of the lengths of corresponding
sides in the two triangles? *Explain* what you notice.

3

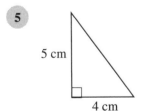

The sides of rectangle ABCD are each increased by 2 cm to form
rectangle PQRS. Are rectangles ABCD and PQRS similar?
Explain your answer.

4 (a) Explain why triangles
ABC and CED are similar.

(b) The lengths BC and CD are in the ratio 2:5.
Find the length DE if it is 9 cm longer than AB.

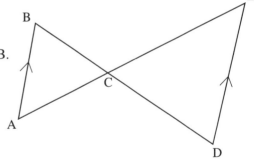

5

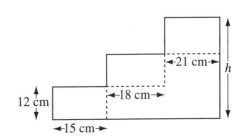

This triangle is similar to a triangle whose 2 shorter lengths are
20 cm and *n* cm. Find the two possible values of *n*.

6 The diagram shows the side view of some steps.
The three rectangles indicated are similar.
Work out the height *h* to the top of the steps.

7 Find the value of x in each diagram below. All lengths are in cm.

(a)

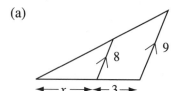

(b)

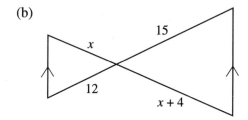